PRAISE FOR
Secrets Savored

"I highly recommend Secrets Savored as an effective reproducible model of Titus 2. The combination of discipleship through biblical devotions and practical home management skills have strengthened our young couples' marriages and thus their families."

Donna Gaines
Pastor's Wife

———————

"When my husband and I moved to a new city, not knowing anyone, Secrets Savored gave me the opportunity to connect with other women also seeking to grow closer to Jesus and discover His purpose for our lives. This ministry brings together women of all ages, backgrounds, and stages of life in such a sweet way that has blessed me."

Sarah Sherlock
Secrets Savored Participant

———————

"Before I knew about Secrets Savored, I prayed that God would allow me to learn from godly women as it says in Titus 2. I am so grateful that He answered my prayers. I have learned so much from the discipling leaders about God's Word and how to be a godly wife and homemaker. I have also learned to follow Christ through the example of the leadership. I cannot thank you enough for showing me how to love Christ supremely and to love my husband."

Jenny McKay
Secrets Savored Participant and Pastor's Wife

———————

"The most important ministry a Christian can have is discipleship, and Secrets Savored is an excellent tool in carrying out that Biblical mandate. In a warm and inviting home setting, young women are led to discover and practice godly living. I have enjoyed being a discipler in a program that balances both the practical and spiritual needs of women. As we talk, eat, study, and have fun together, we develop strong bonds that will last a lifetime. What a blessing!"

Elisa Skinner
Discipling Leader

CREATING COMMUNITY

SECRETS *Savored*

THROUGH SIMPLE HOSPITALITY

Book One

DIANNE DOUGHARTY

Workbook

HIGH BRIDGE BOOKS
HOUSTON

SSECRETS SAVORED
Book One Workbook
Copyright © 2021 by Dianne Lynn Dougharty
All rights reserved.

Scripture quotes are taken from New Living Translation Second Edition, Tyndale House Publishing Company, Carol Stream, Illinois, Copyright ©1968, 1989, 1990, 1991, 1993, 1996, 2004 by Tyndale House Publishing Incorporated. *** Charles Stanley Life Principles Bible Copyright © 2005 by Charles Stanley Holy Bible, New King James Version, Copyright 1982 by Thomas Nelson, Inc.

New American Standard Bible: Ryrie Study Bible, ©1986, 1995 by The Moody Bible Institute. The New Living Translation Parallel Study Bible, ©2011 by Tyndale House Publishers. The Message: The Bible in Contemporary Language Copyright © 2002 by Eugene Peterson. The NIV/Message Parallel Bible Copyright © 2004 The Zondervan Corporation, Grand Rapids, Michigan 49530.

Library of Congress Control Number: 2012945608
ISBN: 978-1-954943-09-4

Graphic Design by *Studio B Print and Design*, Tyler Bedwell

Cover Photography: Jo Laura Bell Photography

Printed in the United States of America U.S. Printing History

First Edition: August 2012

Requests for Information should be addressed to:

Secrets Savored, Inc.
P.O. Box 2257
Cordova, Tennessee 38088

High Bridge Books
Houston, TX

LEADER GUIDE:
The companion Leader Guide with weekly lessons is available on our website at www.secretssavored.org. Go to "Select a Page" and click on shop.

TO ORDER MATERIALS:
To purchase participant workbooks, go to the website at www.secretssavored.org. You will need one book per participant.

TO MY LIFE'S PARTNER, MARK DOUGHARTY

Because of your love, encouragement, sacrifice, and prayers, this ministry exists. I am deeply grateful for your love, not only for me, but for our heavenly Father. You were an incredible example of a man who gave all he had and was to his Savior. You were so very faithful to me, your family, and the One who gave His life for you. I have never known a greater man or prayer warrior. You are deeply missed!

> *"Therefore, brethren, seek out from among you seven men of good reputation, full of the Holy Spirit and wisdom, whom we may appoint over this business; but we will give ourselves continually to prayer and to the ministry of the word."*
>
> Acts 6:3–4 NKJV

On July 31, 2018, my husband, Mark, went home to be with the Lord after an eleven year battle with Multiple Systems Atrophy. He was my biggest fan and a great advocate of this ministry. I am grateful for his love and support and I miss him immensely. I know he is cheering me on from his heavenly home.

WITH GRATITUDE

I am afraid if I try to list the names of all those I owe gratitude, I would neglect someone. So, let me begin with the One without whom none of this would be possible, my heavenly Father. I am grateful to the Lord that He knows best. I would have never dreamed that out of life's most difficult hardship, this ministry would be birthed! Thank you, Father!

The Lord says, 'I will guide you along the best pathway for your life. I will advise you and watch over you.'"

Psalm 32:8 NLT

I want to thank my church, my pastor, and his wife for their love, encouragement, support, and prayers. Thank you to our Women's Ministry staff, who were very helpful as we launched Secrets and continue to be a great help to the ministry. Thank you to the Secrets discipling leadership who have believed in this ministry and the value of using this material in reaching young women for Christ.

To the many young women who participated in the Secrets ministry around the country these past several years, I love you! Thank you for letting us pour into your lives all the secrets we have attained over the years. I pray this study and the lives of the discipling leadership have profoundly impacted your life and home.

A word of gratitude goes to Jo Laura Bell of Jo Laura Bell Photography for our cover and Tyler Bedwell of Studio B Print & Design for designing our logo and formatting the books. I owe you girls a huge thank you for your service, incredible creativity, and patience! To my friend and mentor, Marge, who now resides in heaven, I owe a debt of gratitude for her editing expertise and help. She was always one to go way beyond the "second mile" in order to help a friend.

To our board, thank you for your tireless work and commitment. My heartfelt appreciation goes to the Harry Smith Foundation for the funding to publish the original curriculum material; you were a direct answer to our prayers!

Thank you to those in the body of Christ who gave to Mark and me in so many ways. You believed in this ministry and prayed for us as God led us down a dark road and through deep waters. Your continued support upon Mark's death has been a blessing to me. To my sweet sisters in Christ— thank you for your love, prayers, listening ears, timely hugs, girl moments, the supplied Kleenex, and the laughter, which at times along this journey were much needed and appreciated—I love you!

Mom, I want to thank you and Dad for your encouragement and belief that I could do anything. I never doubted your love or support! To my siblings and Mark's family, I am grateful for your love, support, encouragement, prayers, and belief in God's calling upon my life. Last, but not least, I am very grateful to our daughters, Angela and Kelly, our sons-in-law, and grandchildren for their patience and sacrifice of time away from Mom and Mimi, while I was doing what God had called me to do. How grateful I am for you. You are treasured and loved a bunch!

CONTENTS

Weekly Recipes

INTRODUCTION
to Secrets Savored

As a child, I attended church, but unfortunately, I grew up believing that I had to keep a certain set of rules in order to be a Christian. I was always breaking the rules; therefore, I never felt "good enough" or accepted by God.

My husband, Mark, grew up in the same denomination. Once we were married, we did what most people do who feel that they can never be acceptable to God—we ran from Him. The first few years, we ran hard after the world and away from God. Although our lives were full of things and stuff, we lacked meaning and purpose and peace and joy. We had much, yet we had nothing because we did not have Jesus Christ—who is everything.

> In Romans 11:6 it says, "And since it is through God's kindness, then it is not by their good works. For in that case, God's grace would not be what it really is—free and undeserved." NLT

God tells us that salvation does not come as a result of anything we do, nor because we deserve it, but because of His mercy and grace through the shed blood of His Son, Jesus. It is a free and undeserved gift.

> "For by grace you have been saved through faith. And this is not your own doing; it is a gift of God." Ephesians 2:8 ESV

God intervened in our lives after eleven years of marriage, and Mark was saved. As he studied God's Word, he began to see that it was not by our works or in keeping a set of rules that we are saved, but by the shed blood of Jesus. It was in his accepting Jesus as his personal Lord and Savior that his life was drastically changed. Just a few months after he was saved, I gave my heart and life to Jesus. Thus, my life was forever changed!

The relationship Mark and I had with Christ over the years *determined* the trajectory of our lives, marriage, and family. That relationship sustained me over the eleven years of journeying with him through a dreadful disease called Multiple Systems Atrophy. And, that relationship sustains me now as I adjust to living life without my soulmate and best friend.

In the midst of our journey, God led me to begin a discipling ministry called Secrets Savored. This ministry is based on the verses in Titus 2 that encourage older women to teach younger women by giving them encouragement and strength for living out the life before them. Often, people ask me why the name Secrets Savored? What is the secret? Would you like to know the secret of Secrets Savored?

The **secret** of Secrets Savored is **Jesus**!

In this fatherless, iPhone, Facebook, Twitter, Instagram, self-driven world, Jesus is the only way to true peace and joy. He is the answer for discontentment, insecurity, depression, anxiety, and broken hearts. Secrets Savored is God's tool for reaching young women with the message of relationship versus rules. Through the lives and examples of older godly women and practical and biblical teaching, young women can grow to understand that there is no true peace, joy, contentment, or meaning in life apart from a personal relationship with *Jesus*. I want them to know they are valued by Him, and what they do in life for Him will count and reap a grand reward in the end.

> "Therefore, since we have been made right in God's sight by faith, we have peace with God because of what Jesus Christ our Lord has done for us." Romans 5:1 NLT

I am excited that you are joining this community of women who desire to create a spirit of hospitality and Christlikeness within their lives, homes, and relationships—for the glory of God!

WEEKLY BIBLE STUDY

The main purpose in studying the Bible is so that we will know God.
If we know the Bible, we will thus know the God of the Bible.

The Bible ...

- **INFORMS US**
- **GUIDES US**
- **INSTRUCTS US**
- **CORRECTS AND CONVICTS US**

In Psalms 119:11 it says, "I have hidden your word in my heart that I might not sin against you"(NIV). If we hide scripture and biblical truths in our hearts, it will protect us, and we will always have a word of encouragement and instruction to draw upon.

Women are relational, and women relate to other women. God made us that way. Because of that, we will be studying women in the bible. We will learn biblical principles from each of their lives for living that if followed and applied will protect us from harmful thoughts and actions. Example:

- In studying Sarah, Abraham's wife, we learn about the biblical principle of waiting on God and the consequences of not being willing to wait on Him.

- In studying Rahab, we learn the biblical principle of obedience equals blessing. Her faith led her to trust that God would take care of her and her family. Because she trusted God. He blessed her by placing her in the lineage of Christ.

Many of the women we will be studying over the next few weeks made good choices, but then, others made bad choices. In life, we all make some good and some bad choices. In our study, we will see the blessings of good choices and the consequences of bad choices. God has placed each one within His story so that you and I might relate to them and learn from their lives.

In each week's lesson you will find a question sheet to complete prior to class. The questions will relate to the passage of scripture read for that week's lesson. The study time required should not exceed thirty minutes.

You will receive what you are willing to put into the devotional study each week. Remember hiding God's Word in your heart means you will always have a word from Him for any circumstance you face. May you be blessed as a result of your obedience to study His Word!

Understanding THE BIBLE

Each week, we will be studying women in the Bible. The Bible is a large book covering a lot of information and many topics. Let's get familiar with the books that are found in the Bible—66 in all!

BOOKS OF THE BIBLE:

Old Testament: An account of a Nation: Israel (Jewish people)

Genesis	2 Chronicles	Daniel
Exodus	Ezra	Hosea
Leviticus	Nehemiah	Joel
Numbers	Esther	Amos
Deuteronomy	Job	Obadiah
Joshua	Psalms	Jonah
Judges	Proverbs	Micah
Ruth	Ecclesiastes	Nahum
1Samuel	Song of Solomon	Habakkuk
2 Samuel	Isaiah	Zephaniah
1 Kings	Jeremiah	Haggai
2 Kings	Lamentations	Zechariah
1 Chronicles	Ezekiel	Malachi

New Testament: An account of a Man: Jesus

Matthew	Ephesians	Hebrews
Mark	Philippians	James
Luke	Colossians	1 Peter
John	1 Thessalonians	2 Peter
Acts of the Apostles	2 Thessalonians	1 John
Romans	1 Timothy	2 John
1 Corinthians	2 Timothy	3 John
2 Corinthians	Titus	Jude
Galatians	Philemon	Revelation

Three Easy Steps for Studying the Bible…

As you read the Bible, consider these key steps, and you will gain a better knowledge of what you are reading:

STEP 1: **Observation**—What does the passage say?

- Look carefully at what it says and how it says it.

- Pay attention to the terms, words, etc. Words can have many meanings, but terms are words used in a specific way in a specific context.

- A paragraph is a complete unit of thought.

- The amount of space or the number of chapters or verses given to a specific topic will reveal the importance of that topic.

- *Repetition* is used to demonstrate that something is important. So, watch for repeated words or topics.

- Pay close attention, for example, to certain relationships that appear in the text.

- Be sure you notice the atmosphere, mood, tone, or urgency of the writing.

- *Ask* Who? Who are the people in this passage?
  Ask What? What is happening in this passage?
  Ask Where? Where is this story taking place?
  Ask When? When in time (of day, of the year, in history) is it taking place?

STEP 2: Interpretation—What does the passage mean?

- Ask yourself what is the author's main thought or idea.

- Consider the entire context, verses that come before and after the one you are reading.

- Purchase a good Study Bible and do a cross-reference—look at other scriptures in the Bible noted beside the one you are reading. These verses will help you understand the context of the verse being read. (Example: *The NLT Parallel Study Bible* or the *Ryrie NAS Study Bible*).

- The Bible was written long ago, so when you are trying to figure out what it is saying, you need to understand it from the writer's cultural context. In the front of each book of the Bible, you will find a page informing you of all the details related to that book: The time in which it was written, location, author, etc. Reading this page will give you a better knowledge of what you will be reading.

- Read commentaries by Bible scholars. These books can help you understand scripture. Example: *Matthew Henry's Commentary on the Whole Bible*

STEP 3: Application—What am I going to do about what the passage says and means?

- We study the Bible for the purpose of application. Applying what we have learned will change our lives. Obedience to God's Word will assist us in growing more like Jesus Christ.

- After we have observed a passage and interpreted it to the best of our ability, we must then apply its truth to our own life.

- Asking the following questions will help you to better apply what you have learned:
  How does the truth I have read affect my relationship with God?
  How does this truth affect my relationship with others?
  How does this truth affect me?
  How does this truth affect my response to the enemy, Satan?

- The key to applying what you have read is putting into practice what God has taught you in your study. You may not be able to daily, consciously apply everything you have learned in Bible study, but you can consciously apply *some* of what you have learned.

- God blesses our efforts to apply His truth to our lives. Through our application of those truths, we will be conformed into the image of Jesus Christ.

Week One

ORGANIZING YOUR KITCHEN

A Heart Set ON LEARNING

*I*n the summer of 1969, between my seventh and eighth grade year, my family moved back to Nashville, Tennessee, where we had lived prior to my parents attending the University of Kansas. Beginning a new school and making friends at that age was quite a challenge; let's just say it was the pits! I was looking for ways to meet the girls in my grade, so when I had a chance to sign up for Home Economics, an all-girls class, I took it. This particular class is probably not familiar to today's young women, but yes, they did actually offer a class where young women could discover the foundations of keeping a home.

It was easy for me to make friends in my Home Economics class because each day we worked as a team to accomplish the assignment given to us. When you work together you become friends. I really enjoyed going to the class. It was a nice change from English, Math, History, and the rest of my courses.

As a part of our overall grade, we were expected to eat what we had prepared. I will never forget the day we cooked fried okra. Okay, it is finally time for me to confess. I found the pockets in my apron—yes, we were required to wear an apron—quite handy that day for dispensing my fried okra from my plate to the corner trash can. Confession is good for the soul. To this day, I have absolutely no desire to eat fried okra.

In Home Economics, students worked together to learn how to bake, cook, and do basic sewing. Along with learning practical homemaking skills, our teacher also taught proper etiquette. Today, we seldom hear the word etiquette, let alone know what it means. *Etiquette* is the prescribed rules, form and practices, established for behavior in polite society or in official or professional life. Now you know!

---

*S*ecrets Savored is not a school course; there will be no tests or final exams. You will not be forced to eat what you cook. We, as leaders, are not trained or certified teachers, just women who have, through the years, acquired wisdom, knowledge, skills, and numerous secrets in the area of being a wife, mom, and homemaker. This will be a class where you can work side-by-side with young and older women in learning how to bake, cook, sew, organize a home, etc.

In the weeks to follow, there will be some subjects concerning homemaking you will love and others you will not like at all. That's okay! I love to iron, but I really dislike vacuuming; however, there are times when I have to do both. Over the years, the vacuuming has occurred only when there was no one else there to do it for me!

We, the leadership, would ask *only* three things of you:

- To faithfully attend each week

- To participate in the activities

- To have *a heart set on learning*

We are so excited that you have chosen to be a part of this Secrets class! This study is designed to be fun, informative, and educational. You will be drawn to the subjects you love and for those you do not like, you will probably do anyway, out of necessity. Such is the life of a woman!

Whatcha Know
ACTIVITY SHEET

TRUE OR FALSE:

_____ 1. Decaffeinated coffee is made from coffee beans that have been soaked or steamed to allow all the caffeine to diffuse from the beans. In the process, 97 percent of the caffeine is removed.

_____ 2. Cinnamon sticks can be grated with a grater that has small holes and then used as ground cinnamon.

_____ 3. There is no difference between chopping, mincing, cubing, and dicing in cooking.

_____ 4. A frittata is an Italian sandwich that resembles a crustless quiche.

_____ 5. Frosting is the same as icing.

_____ 6. There is a difference between French bread and Italian bread.

_____ 7. Rosemary, cilantro, tarragon, and thyme are among some of the strongest herbs.

_____ 8. Dark and light molasses are interchangeable in cooking.

_____ 9. To prevent sliced peaches from browning, sprinkle with lemon juice and toss lightly.

_____ 10. A truffle is a layered English dessert usually served in a glass dish.

_____ 11. The time a turkey cooks is based on the weight of the turkey.

_____ 12. Bleached flour is wheat flour that has been treated with a whitening agent and can be used interchangeably with all-purpose flour.

_____ 13. If a recipe calls for buttermilk and you do not have any, there is no substitute, and you are out of luck!

_____ 14. Three medium apples are equal to 1½ cups of chopped apples.

_____ 15. One half cup of Splenda is equal to one half cup of granulated sugar.

_____ 16. Fondant is a French word referring to a food that is cooked at the table in a ceramic lined metal bowl.

KRAZY KITCHEN TRIVIA
ACTIVITY SHEET

1. This cookie debuted in 1912, and since then, 362 billion have been sold; it is considered the best-selling cookie in the United States.

2. What company did the name Nabisco originate from?

3. In 1853, George Crum was the chef at an elegant resort in Saratoga, New York. He was the creator of a snack food now consumed by millions. In 1860, he opened his first restaurant featuring these snacks in baskets on every table.

4. This food item is second in human consumption only to rice.

5. In 1932, a company was started in Nashville and is now the largest seller of an American salty snack food.

6. Turbinado and muscovado are names of what type of food?

7. This kitchen instrument has a broad, flat, flexible blade used to mix, spread, and lift in cooking or baking. The term for this instrument originated in England in 1525.

8. This kitchen appliance was invented in 1908 by Herbert Johnson, an engineer for the Hobart Manufacturing Company. In 1919, Mr. Johnson started his own company manufacturing his eighty-quart machine that would be used in bakeries all over the world.

9. It takes twenty-one pounds of fresh, wholesome cow's milk to make one pound of this creamy dairy product.

10. In early times, this kitchen cookware stood on three legs, which allowed it to be positioned over an open fire.

11. This food product was mentioned often in the Bible and has been around for hundreds of years. It is often enjoyed with a meal.

12. The jingle from this cleaning product ad was the longest running jingle on American television and was sung by Don Cherry and Betty Bryan. This cleaner was the first liquid cleaner to be sold in a plastic bottle.

13. This cleaning product was introduced in 1958 and was the first such product to be released in a spray form.

14. Prior to 1797, these cleaning tools were handmade using grass, hay, straw, fine twigs, and corn husks.

15. This screw-neck bottle was patented by John Mason.

16. German engineer Carl von Linde patented the first process of liquefying gas in 1876, which is the basic technology of this kitchen appliance.

17. In 1801, Josiah Bent Bakery in Milton, Massachusetts, created this bakery product that has accompanied a bowl of soup for years.

18. This basic pantry product appears in 97 percent of American homes. The first recipe was printed in Elizabeth Smith's *The Complete Housewife* in 1727. It called for anchovies, shallots, vinegar, white wine, sweet spices, pepper, and lemon peel. More recent recipes call for tomato, vinegar, sugar, salt, allspice, cloves, and cinnamon. It is considered a moderate health benefit, as it contains lycopene.

What Does an
ORGANIZED KITCHEN LOOK LIKE?

On your countertop or easily accessible for cooking:

- Sea salt in a small container or in a shaker

- Pepper in grinder or shaker

- Cutting board near stovetop

- Stand mixer, where space allows

- Utensil holder for wooden spoons, spatulas, etc.

- Canisters for sugar, flour, etc.

- Dishes in cabinet closest to dishwasher

- Drinking glasses in cabinet close to dishwasher and refrigerator

- Spices and baking ingredients—granulated sugar, brown sugar, confectioners' sugar, baking soda, baking powder, vanilla, etc., in cabinet closest to mixer and stovetop. <u>Note</u>: Not directly over stovetop.

- Place pots, pans, and skillets for cooking in cabinet or drawer closest to stovetop

- Place all baking pans in cabinet closest to oven or in drawer under stove

- For kitchen drawers: Place kitchen towels near sink, silverware near table and/or dishwasher, and cooking utensils/knives near stove and work area

EXTRA HELPS: Use plastic or wooden trays in drawers to organize silverware, knives, and utensils. This will keep them from sliding around and will be easier for you to retrieve when needed. If you are limited on space, use plastic storage containers to store flour, granulated sugar, confectioners' sugar and brown sugar along with other baking items. Use canisters if counters are large enough to accommodate.

RECIPES: Place all of your recipes in a file on your computer. Photo albums (4x6 pockets) can also be used to store special recipes. Label each file or album with one of the following headings: *Entrees–Vegetables, Appetizers–Breads, Soups–Salads,* and *Dessert.* The recipes will be easier to locate, and you will always have them protected in your computer or placed within a photo album.

Have you asked the question, why cook?
Here are some answers to your question:

1. If you are married, it is a way to minister to your husband and family. If single, it is a great way to minister to your family and friends.

2. It is a great way to minister to those outside your family. Having people into your home/apartment, and preparing a meal for them, can be a tremendous witness to the lost world and a great ministry to those you care about.

3. It provides time for you to be together as a family and as friends, gathering around the table spending valuable time together and making memories.

4. It is a much healthier choice for you and your family.

5. It is more cost efficient than eating out.

FOOD SAFETY SHEET [1]

To ensure that the foods you serve are safe to eat, follow these basic and important safety rules.

- **KEEP IT CLEAN**. Before handling any food, thoroughly wash your hands in hot, soapy water. Make sure all work surfaces, cutting boards, knives, and any other utensils have been cleaned in hot, soapy water. After handling raw food, clean hands and utensils in hot, soapy water.

  Cutting boards can be sanitized with a mixture of 1 teaspoon chlorine bleach in one quart of water. Allow the bleach-water to stand on the cutting board for several minutes before rinsing. Let the board air dry or dry with clean paper towels.

- **KEEP IT SEPARATE**. Do not cross-contaminate foods—do not allow the juices of raw meats, poultry, and fish to come in contact with other foods. Reusing a cutting board, countertop, plate, knife, sink, or other utensil that came in contact with raw meat without first thoroughly washing it in hot, soapy water can cause cross-contamination. Never reuse packaging material, such as foam meat trays or plastic wrap.

  It is not recommended that you wash any raw meat before cooking: poultry, lamb, veal, pork, or seafood. Any bacteria that may be present on the surface of these foods will be destroyed by properly cooking the food. Washing any of these items will contaminate the sink, which can cause cross-contamination if not cleaned right away with bleach.

- **KEEP IT AT THE RIGHT TEMPERATURE**. Always keep hot foods hot and cold foods cold. Cooked foods and uncooked foods that require refrigeration should be left at room temperature for only two hours and only one hour on a hot day. To keep foods hot—to at least 140°F—use warming trays, slow cookers, and chafing dishes. Use ice to keep foods cold.

- **FOOD SAFETY TIP:** For sanitation purposes, purchase several different colored plastic cutting boards. Use a different color for different items: green for fruits and vegetables, red for meat, and yellow for chicken.

- **EXPIRATION DATES:** To better understand labels and expiration dates on food products, go to stilltasty.com, click on "Shelf Life" and scroll to the article on expiration dates.

[1] *The Taste of Home Cookbook* (Reiman Media Group Inc., 2009).

What I Learned Today

KITCHEN BASICS

A KNIFE AND A SHOE

I grew up in a home with a very creative and frugal dad. We had very little money, so he was always looking for ways to fix things with the supplies that were available in our home. Sometimes it worked and sometimes it didn't. One time, he worked on a faucet in the kitchen; we are not sure exactly what he did or what tools he used. We do know that after he finished, the hot-water side was cold, the cold-water side was hot, and it took a sledgehammer to raise the handle! We just laughed and figured eventually the handle would loosen, and over time, we would get used to the hot being cold and the cold being hot!

Have you ever tried to peel a potato with a table knife? If you have, you know that typically you end up losing half of the potato! Have you ever tried to drive a nail into a wall with a rubber soled shoe instead of a hammer? It doesn't work very well, does it? Using the proper utensils or tools makes the job you are doing much easier. Homemaking is much easier if we have the proper *equipment* and if we are able to find them. Where was that hammer, anyway? It should have been in the catchall drawer, along with the peeler, the rubber bands, the children's schoolwork, the pens, etc. You know that drawer, don't you? Everyone has one of those drawers, right? Maybe the proper name would be the junk drawer. When it comes to having an organized kitchen, having the right *equipment* and being able to find it is very important.

My dad grew up in a home with twelve siblings during the Depression. This could be the reason he was so frugal, and why he never threw anything away! The chaos of having piles of things and stuff everywhere never bothered him; on the other hand, my mom liked things neat and organized. I take after my mom. I was born with a mind that thinks *organization.*

O ver the years, I have discovered that some people are naturally organized, and others are not. Mark and I were very different when it came to organizing—whether it was our time or things. When we would go out to run errands, I had already thought through a plan for the most efficient route. Mark had no plan—he was just along for the ride and to accomplish the task ahead of us. His mind did not work the same way as mine when it came to organization, and for that, he was grateful. Because his mind did not automatically think organizationally, he escaped the responsibility of loading the car each time we headed out on a trip. He would often say, "There's no way all that stuff is going into that trunk." Somehow, it all went in! Like they say, "Where there's a will and an organized mind, there's a way."

Having a work area *organized* helps you be more efficient. Your kitchen is a work area. Sure, you have fun there and, yes, you make memories there, but the main activity of a kitchen is work. Having the right equipment helps you be more efficient and accomplish the goal for which you are in the kitchen— to provide meals for your family. So, if your hammer and your peeler are buried in the junk drawer and you have to use a table knife to peel your potatoes, the work will not get done as efficiently, and dinner may never be served!

The
GADGET GAME

1. _____

2. _____

3. _____

4. _____

5. _____

6. _____

7. _____

8. _____

9. _____

10. _____

Basic
KITCHEN UTENSILS

WHISK:

Batter Whisk

Balloon Whisk—Large, medium, and small

Flat Whisk

FOR PASTRY:

Fluted Pastry Wheel

Marble Pastry Board

Mesh Sugar Shaker

Nonstick Rolling Mat

Pastry Bag

Pastry Brush Set

Pastry Scraper

Piecrust Shield

Rolling Pin—Maple, marble, or silicone

Stainless-Steel

BAKING:

Cooling Racks

Hand-Held Electric Mixer

Mini Offset Stainless-Steel Spatula

Offset Stainless-Steel Icing Spatula

Scoops—A variety of sizes for cookies, muffins etc.

Set of Glass Measuring Cups with Spout for Liquids

Set of Metal or Plastic Measuring Cups

Set of Metal or Plastic Measuring Spoons

Set of Mixing Bowls—Glass or hard plastic

Set of Rubber Spatulas/Silicone Spatulas—All sizes and shapes

Sifter

Silicone Baking Mats

SPOONS:

Pasta Spoon

Slotted Spoon

Soup Ladle

Spoonula

Sturdy Metal Spoons

Wooden Spoons/Plastic Spoons

KNIVES: Made from high-carbon stainless steel

Chef's Knife—Eight-inch or ten-inch blade

Knife Sharpener

One Serrated Knife

Paring Knife—Three-inch or four-inch blade

Pizza Cutter

Set of Steak Knives

Vegetable Peeler

COLANDERS AND STRAINERS:

Colander—Plastic or steel

Set of Nested Varying Size Strainers—All in stainless steel, also works well as a flour sifter

GRATERS:

Grater

Micro Plane Grater

Micro Plane Parmesan Cheese Grater

Micro Plane Ultra-Coarse Grater

Vegetable Peeler—Swivel-blade Vegetable Peeler

TONGS:

Non-Stick Tongs

Silicone Locking Tongs

Stainless Steel Tongs

MISCELLANEOUS:

Can Opener

Cheese Slicer

Garlic Press

Hot Mitts/Pads

Ice Cream Scoop

Kitchen Shears

Kitchen Timer

Lettuce Spinner

Meat Mallet/Tenderizer

Mix-n-Chop

Paper Towel Holder

Set of 100 Percent Cotton Dishcloths

Set of 100 Percent Cotton Towels

Silicone Basting Brush

Trivets

Vegetable Brush

Bridal Registry:
UTENSIL AND KITCHEN EQUIPMENT LIST

SMALL UTENSILS:

Can Opener

Cookie Scoop

Garlic Press

Ice Cream Scoop

Measuring Spoons—long and narrow to t into a spice bottle

Pampered Chef's Mix-n-Chop

Paring Knives

Pizza Cutter

Plastic Spoons

Salad Tongs

Serving Spoon—regular and slotted

Set of Stainless-Steel Knives and a Knife Sharpener

Set of Measuring Cups—glass for liquids and metal for dry ingredients Firm Spatula

Small Spatula

Spoonula

Vegetable Peeler

Whisk—set of three sizes

Wooden or Bamboo Spoons

PREPARATION:

Extra Large Mixing Bowl

Mini Cutting Board

Plastic Cutting Board

Set of Cooking Pans—variety of sizes

Set of Mixing Bowls—glass or plastic

Wood Cutting Board

STORAGE:

Corning Ware® or Pyrex® Set

Extra Large Measuring Cup with Lid

Rubbermaid Set

Storage Units for Spice Cans/Bottles

SMALL APPLIANCES:

Food Processor

Multiple Crock-Pots—small, medium, large Blender

Stand Mixer

Waffle Iron

BAKING UTENSILS:

Cookie Sheets—set of two

Cooling Racks

Corning Ware® or Set of Pyrex,® 9x13—variety of sizes

Mini Loaf Pans—set of four

Muffin Pan

Round Cake Pans—set of two

9x13 Baking Pan

Cooking and Baking
SUBSTITUTIONS [2]

BAKING POWDER	1 t	½ t cream of tartar plus ¼ t baking soda
BROTH	1 cup	1 cup hot water with 1 bouillon cube
BUTTERMILK	1 cup	1 T lemon juice or 1 T vinegar, add milk to = 1 cup
CAJUN SEASONING	1 t	¼ t cayenne pepper; ½ t dried thyme; ¼ t dried basil and 1 minced garlic clove
CHOCOLATE, semisweet	1 oz. square	1 square (1oz.) unsweetened choc. plus 1 T sugar or 3 T semisweet chocolate chips
CHOCOLATE	1 oz. square	3 T baking cocoa plus 1 T butter
CORNSTARCH	1 T	2 T all-purpose flour (for thickening)
CORN SYRUP, dark	1 cup	¾ cup light syrup plus ¼ cup molasses
CORN SYRUP, light	1 cup	1 cup sugar plus 1 cup water
CRACKER CRUMBS	1 cup	1 cup dry breadcrumbs
CREAM (half and half)	1 cup	1 T melted butter and enough whole milk to equal a cup
EGG	1 whole	2 egg whites or 2 egg yolks or ¼ cup egg substitute
FLOUR, cake	1 cup	1 cup minus 2 T (⅞ cup) all-purpose flour
FLOUR, self-rising	1 cup	1½ t baking powder, ½ t salt, and enough all-purpose flour to equal 1 cup
GARLIC (fresh)	1 clove	⅛ t garlic powder, ½ t minced garlic (in a jar), dried garlic flakes, or garlic juice
GINGER ROOT, fresh	1 t	¼ t ground ginger
HONEY	1 cup	1¼ cups sugar plus ¼ cup water
LEMON JUICE	1 t	¼ t cider vinegar
LEMON PEEL	1 t	½ t lemon extract
MILK, whole	1 cup	½ cup evaporated milk plus ½ c water or 1 cup water plus ⅓ cup powdered milk
MOLASSES	1 cup	1 cup honey

[2] *The Taste of Home Cookbook* (Reiman Media Group Inc., 2009).

MUSTARD	1 T	½ T ground mustard plus 2 t cider or white vinegar
ONION	1 small	1 t onion powder or 1 T dried minced onion
POULTRY SEASONING	1 t	¾ t rubbed sage plus ¼ t dried thyme
SOUR CREAM	1 cup	1 cup plain yogurt (Greek yogurt is thicker)
SUGAR	1 cup	1 cup packed brown sugar or 2 cups sifted confectioners' sugar
TOMATO JUICE	1 cup	½ cup tomato sauce plus ½ cup water
TOMATO SAUCE	2 cups	¾ cup tomato paste plus 1 cup water
YEAST	1 pkg.	1 cake (⅝ oz.) compressed yeast or ¼ oz. active dry yeast

---

OTHERS:

SWEETENED CONDENSED MILK	1 cup	⅓ cup evaporated milk, ¾ cup sugar, 2 t butter, heat until sugar and butter dissolve
YOGURT	1 cup	1 cup buttermilk
KETCHUP	1 cup	1 cup tomato sauce, ½ cup sugar, 2 T vinegar
MAYONNAISE	1 cup	For salads and dressings: 1 cup plain yogurt or 1 cup sour cream
VINEGAR	½ cup	½ cup red wine vinegar
ALLSPICE	1 t	½ t ground cinnamon plus ½ t ground cloves
APPLE PIE SPICE	1 t	½ t ground cinnamon, ¼ t ground nutmeg, plus ⅛ t ground clove
CHIVES, chopped	1 T	1 T chopped green onion tops
PUMPKIN PIE SPICE	1 t	½ t ground cinnamon, ¼ t ground ginger, ⅛ t ground allspice, plus ⅛ t ground nutmeg
WORCESTERSHIRE	1 t	1 t bottled steak sauce

Basic Pantry Needs

BAKING:

Almond Extract

Baking powder

Baking soda

Brown sugar

Cake flour

Canola oil

Chocolate chips

Cocoa powder

Confectioners' sugar

Cornstarch

Corn syrup

Flour (all purpose)

Granulated sugar

Honey

Nonstick spray

Nuts

Shortening

Table salt

Vanilla extract

MEATS:

Canned chicken

Canned tuna

OTHER:

Almond Butter

Breakfast cereal

Cookies

Frozen green vegetables

Ice cream or popsicles

COOKING:

Balsamic vinegar

Breadcrumbs

Canned beans: green, pinto, black, etc.

Canned diced tomatoes

Chicken/Beef stock or broth

Cream of Chicken soup (or make your own)

Cream of Mushroom soup (or make your own)

Olive oil

Pasta: Rigatoni and Spaghetti

Plain or Apple Cider vinegar

Rice—Any variety

Soy sauce

Spaghetti sauce/Alfredo sauce

Tomato paste/Tomato sauce

Worcestershire sauce

Dale's Marinade

Maple Syrup

Peanut Butter

Salad dressing

Snacks

QUICK MIXES:

Macaroni and cheese

Pizza mix

REFRIGERATOR AND FRESH INGREDIENTS:

Butter

Buttermilk

Cheese—Cheddar, Parmesan, Colby Jack, etc.

Cream Cheese

Deli Meat

Fresh fruit

Fresh vegetables Garlic, fresh or minced in jar

Fresh Tomato

Jams and jellies

Ketchup

Lemons or lemon juice

Lettuce or Spinach

Mayonnaise

Milk/Half and half

Mustard—a variety

Onions—variety fresh or frozen

Pickles—a variety

Plain Yogurt or Sour Cream

Pickles—a variety

Salad Dressing—a variety

SEASONINGS:

Allspice

Basil

Bay leaves—Fresh or powdered

Beef and Chicken bouillon (low-sodium)

Cayenne pepper

Celery seed or salt

Chili powder

Cinnamon

Cloves—Ground

Cumin

Curry powder

Dale's marinade

Food coloring

Garlic powder

Ground black pepper

Ground red pepper

Italian seasoning

Pickles—A variety

Onion powder

Oregano

Paprika

Parsley

Red pepper flakes

Sage

Salt

Taco seasoning

Thyme

RECIPES

Creamy Fruit Dip

1 (7 ounce) jar marshmallow cream

2 (8 ounce) packages cream cheese, softened

1 (8 ounce) container sour cream

1 (14 ounce) can sweetened condensed milk

Combine all the ingredients in a blender and blend until smooth. Refrigerate at least one hour. Serve with assorted fruit. Divide recipe in half and use sour cream in one half of the batch; substitute yogurt in the other half. <u>Note</u>: This recipe makes a large amount. Consider cutting the recipe in half for a small group.

RECIPES USING PANTRY LIST

Chicken Parmesan

4 tablespoons olive oil

1 small onion, cut into thin slices

Salt and pepper to taste

2 tablespoons sugar

4 boneless chicken breasts

2 tablespoons balsamic vinegar

2 large eggs, beaten with 1 tablespoon water

1 jar of favorite spaghetti sauce

½ cup flour, approximately

1 cup Italian breadcrumbs

2 tablespoons Italian seasoning

1 cup Mozzarella cheese, grated

½ cup Parmesan cheese, grated

1 package spaghetti noodles

Preheat oven to 350°F. Place 2 tablespoons of olive oil in a large skillet. Warm over medium-low heat. Place sliced onion into the skillet; sprinkle with salt, pepper, and sugar. Cook with lid on for approximately 20 to 30 minutes, stirring occasionally until onions are a caramel color. While onions are cooking, tenderize chicken with a meat mallet, place on plate. <u>Note:</u> To save mess, put chicken breasts in a plastic zipper-lock bag to tenderize.

Meanwhile, you will need three containers: a bowl in which to whisk the egg mixture, another bowl for the flour and the Italian seasoning, and the third bowl for the breadcrumbs. Heat skillet over medium heat, and pour in the remaining 2 tablespoons of olive oil. Once hot, place chicken breasts, one at a time, into flour mixture, turn to coat, place into the egg mixture, and finally into the breadcrumbs. Place each breast in skillet of hot oil, searing on each side for 4 to 5 minutes. Turn each breast only once. Place in a casserole dish, top with caramelized onions, cover the chicken with spaghetti sauce, and top with cheeses. Bake for 20 to 25 minutes until cheese is melted and golden brown. Cook the spaghetti noodles according to directions on package. See the following shortcut.

Shortcut: Mix the Parmesan cheese and breadcrumbs together and top only with the Mozzarella. If you do not like the flavor of the onions, they are not crucial to the recipe.

Items not on pantry list: Chicken breast, Mozzarella cheese

Buttery Beef Stroganoff

2 pounds round steak, substitute with ground beef, cooked and drained

¼ cup all-purpose flour

½ cup butter

1½ teaspoon salt

⅛ teaspoon pepper

½ cup water

1 (10 ounce) can cream of mushroom soup

¾ cup sour cream

¼ cup milk

Hot cooked egg noodles

Fresh parsley for garnish

Cut steak into 2-inch by ½-inch strips; coat with flour and brown in butter in large skillet. Salt and pepper strips. Stir occasionally. Cover and simmer for 45 minutes or until almost tender; stir occasionally. Mix in soup and simmer uncovered 30 minutes or until meat is tender. Stir in sour cream and milk; cook until thoroughly heated. Serve over hot noodles. Garnish with fresh parsley.

Note: For a healthier dish, make your own cream of mushroom soup. See www.100daysrealfood.com.

Items not on the pantry list: Round steak (Ground beef) and noodles

Hawaiian Chicken

4 to 6 chicken breasts, tenderized

1 (8 ounce) can of crushed pineapple, drained

¼ cup chicken broth

¼ cup spicy brown mustard

¼ cup honey

3 tablespoons butter, melted

½ teaspoon paprika

Preheat oven to 375°F. Tenderize chicken, one breast at a time, with a meat mallet inside a zipper-lock bag. Remove chicken from plastic bag and place in 9x13 casserole dish coated with cooking spray. In a bowl, mix together pineapple, broth, spicy mustard, honey, and butter. Spoon this mixture over the chicken breasts and top with paprika. Bake uncovered for 35 to 45 minutes.

Note: In order to enhance the flavor and make your dinner time go smoother, make this dish in the morning and store in refrigerator all day. Sauce will soak into the chicken and act as a marinade. It's great with white rice and a vegetable of your choice.

Items not on the pantry list: Chicken and crushed pineapple

EVE
A Woman of Influence

Biblical Principle: Christian women must guard wisely and carefully the influence they have over the men in their lives.

Read Genesis Chapter 1:26, 2:7—9, 15—25, and Chapter 3.

1. What are some key truths discovered in these verses?

2. Who did the serpent approach first? Why?

3. What mistakes did Eve make?

4. Women have great influence over men; we have the ability to influence them for good or for bad. Write down ways that Eve wrongly influenced Adam.

5. Give prayerful consideration as to the men in your life and the intent of your heart in influencing them. Write down what God revealed to you that you should do differently.

6. What lessons have you learned from Eve that you will apply to your life?

What I Learned Today

Week Three

KITCHEN LINGO

Introduction

FLOATING IN SYRUP

Our two girls married within two years of each other. One of the first major decisions they faced as a young married couple was which holiday to spend with which family. It is one of those major decisions that can often cause newlyweds to have their first serious fight. Maybe some of you can relate. Mark and I had that fight! To be honest, when I was young and newly married, I was not fair to my in-laws. After all, I wanted to be with my family. Isn't it expected that the new groom will do whatever his new bride wants? I have, in my later years, regretted that I robbed my in-laws of time with their son and grandchildren. So, in an effort to make up for it, and because I did not want my girls to have the same regret, I encouraged them to be with us every other Christmas. The year they were at their in-laws for Christmas, we would make Thanksgiving our BIG holiday.

Our younger daughter, Kelly, got married two years after her older sister married. So, the girls decided that fall that they would both go to their in-laws for Christmas. Due to their decision, we had to quickly plan our Thanksgiving and Christmas all in one. We had a few things to consider: Would we have our traditional Christmas breakfast on Thanksgiving morning? Would we open presents the morning of Thanksgiving or the evening of Thanksgiving? Would we have turkey and the traditional Thanksgiving meal or serve something different? So many decisions! We finally made our decisions and put together our plan and menu for Thanksgiving Day. A traditional Thanksgiving meal is what was decided upon.

We divided the responsibilities for cooking. Kelly was to prepare two items and one was going to be a dessert. On Wednesday before the BIG day, we set out to do all the cooking and baking with three little people under three around our feet. I was making a cake and a traditional pumpkin pie, so Kelly decided that a fruit pie would be good. Remembering how wonderful her mother-in-law's apple pie was, she called to get her recipe. Once that was in hand, she set out for the grocery store to purchase the ingredients. She was excited about her choice, since her dad loved apple pie with ice cream, and this was a recipe she had never made before.

___

The crust was absolutely perfect and from scratch. There was no frozen crust going to be used for this pie! She worked hard slicing the apples and combining all the ingredients. Once the oven was Preheated, she placed this beautiful pie in to cook. It smelled so good baking along with the turkey. After a while, Kelly began to notice the syrup bubbling up and over the crust. We grabbed a cookie sheet to place under the pie, still bubbling and bubbling! Finally, the apples were cooked and the crust was a beautiful golden brown. She removed it from the oven only to discover that the apples were floating in syrup. Our first thought was that those were really juicy apples! But our second thought was, what went wrong? Kelly got out the recipe and began to read it. She then called her mother-in-law to go back over all the ingredients and their measurements. I heard her say, "Oh, that's it!"

You see, the recipe had called for a half cup of sugar, and Kelly had written down one and a half cups—enough sugar for three pies! After the pie cooled, the apples were still floating in syrup. The men in the family felt sorry for Kelly and each ate a piece. We all laughed at the sight of that pie, and Kelly learned a valuable cooking lesson that Thanksgiving—accurate measuring is the key to the success of a recipe!

Cooking Terms MATCHING GAME

	Roux	1. Italian term used to describe pasta that is cooked until if offers a slight resistance to the bite.
	Truss	2. To moisten foods during cooking with pan drippings or special sauce to add flavor and prevent drying.
	Emulsify	3. To immerse in rapidly boiling water and cook slightly.
	Clarify	4. To cook slowly in a small amount of liquid in a covered pan on the stovetop or in the oven. Generally used for less tender cuts of meat.
	Al dente	5. To split foods, such as chicken breasts, boneless meat, or shrimp, lengthwise in half, leaving the meat attached along one side.
	Knead	6. To separate and remove solids from liquid, thus making it clear.
	Deglaze	7. To dissolve the thin glaze of juices and brown bits on the surface of a pan in which food has been fried, sauteed, or roasted. To do this, add liquid and stir and scrape over high heat, thereby adding flavor to the liquid for use as a sauce.
	Braise	8. To sprinkle or coat with flour or other fine substance.
	Baste	9. To combine through a whisking action two liquids that traditionally separate, such as oil and vinegar, into a uniform mixture.
	Glaze	10. To secure poultry with string or skewers, to hold its shape while cooking.
	Dredge	11. To cook with a thin sugar syrup cooked to crack stage; mixture may be thickened slightly to cover with a thin, glossy icing.
	Blanch	12. To cut vegetables, fruits, or cheeses into thin strips.
	Poach	13. To work and press dough with the palms of the hands, or mechanically to develop the gluten in the flour.
	Butterfly	14. To cook very gently in hot liquid kept just below the boiling point.
	Julienne	15. A French term for a mixture of flour and fat that is cooked together until brown and used to thicken gumbos, soups, and sauces.

Glossary of COOKING TERMS [3]

AL DENTE: Italian term used to describe pasta that is cooked until it offers a slight resistance to the bite

AU JUS: Natural juices that collect while roasting meats

BAKE: To cook by dry heat, usually in the oven

BARBECUE: Usually used to refer to grilling done outdoors or over an open charcoal or wood fire. More specifically, barbecue refers to long, slow, direct-heat cooking, including liberal basting with a barbecue sauce

BASTE: To moisten foods during cooking with pan drippings or special sauce to add flavor and prevent drying

BATTER: A mixture containing flour and liquid, thin enough to pour or thick enough to be dropped from a spoon

BEAT: To mix rapidly in order to make a mixture smooth and light by incorporating as much air as possible

BLANCH: To immerse in rapidly boiling water and cook slightly

BLEND: To incorporate two or more ingredients thoroughly

BOIL: To heat a liquid until bubbles break continually on the surface

BONE: To remove raw or cooked meat from bones

BRAISE: To cook slowly in a small amount of liquid in a covered pan on the stovetop or in the oven. Generally used for less tender cuts of meat

BREADING: A coating of fine breadcrumbs or crackers used on meat, fish, or vegetables

BROIL: To cook on a grill under strong, direct heat

BROWN: To cook foods in a small amount of fat over medium to high heat until the food becomes brown, sealing in juices and creating rich pan drippings

BUTTERFLY: To split foods, such as chicken breasts, boneless meat, or shrimp, lengthwise in half, leaving the meat attached along one side

CARAMELIZE: To heat sugar in order to turn it brown and give it a special taste

CHOP: To cut solids into pieces with a sharp knife or other chopping device

[3] *The Taste of Home Cookbook* (Reiman Media Group Inc., 2009).

CHILL: To cool foods to below room temperature (40°F or less), by placing them in the refrigerator, freezer, or an ice bath

CLARIFY: To separate and remove solids from a liquid, thus making it clear

COAT: To dip or roll foods in flour, breadcrumbs, sugar, or a sauce until covered

COMBINE: To place several ingredients in a single bowl or container and mix thoroughly

COOL: To bring foods to room temperature (About 70°F)

CREAM: To soften a fat, especially butter, by beating it at room temperature. Butter and sugar are often creamed together, making a smooth, soft paste

CRISP-TENDER: A stage of vegetable cooking where the vegetables are cooked until they are crunchy, yet tender enough to be pierced with a fork

CUBE: To cut foods into ½-inch to 1-inch square pieces

CURE: To preserve meats by drying and salting and/or smoking

DASH: A measurement less than ⅛ teaspoon that is used for herbs, spices, or hot pepper sauce. This is not an accurate measurement

DEGLAZE: To dissolve the thin glaze of juices and brown bits on the surface of a pan in which food has been fried, sautéed, or roasted. To do this, add liquid and stir and scrape over high heat, thereby adding flavor to the liquid for use as a sauce

DEGREASE: To remove fat from the surface of stews, soups, or stock; cool in the refrigerator so that fat hardens and is easily removed

DICE: To cut food in small cubes of uniform size and shape

DIRECT HEAT: To cook foods on outdoor grill directly over coals or heat source

DISSOLVE: To cause a dry substance to pass into solution in a liquid

DREDGE: To sprinkle or coat with flour or other fine substance

DRIZZLE: To sprinkle drops of liquid lightly over food in a casual manner

DRESS: To toss salads with salad dressing; to remove the internal organs of fish, poultry, or game

DRIPPINGS: The juices and melted fat that collect in the bottom of the pan in which meat is cooked. These can be used in gravies and sauces

DUST: To sprinkle food with dry ingredients. Use a strainer or a jar with a perforated cover, or try the good, old-fashioned way of shaking things together in a paper bag

DUTCH OVEN: A multipurpose cooking pot that can range in size from 5 to 8 quarts and is used to roast meat, cook soups and stews, boil pasta, or steam vegetables

EMULSIFY: To combine through a whisking action two liquids that traditionally separate, such as oil and vinegar, into a uniform mixture

FILET: A boneless cut of meat

FILLET: As a verb—to remove the bones from meat or fish. A fillet is the piece of flesh after it has been boned

FLAKE: To break lightly into small pieces

FLAMBÉ: To flame foods by dousing in some form of portable alcohol and setting alight

FOLD: To incorporate a delicate substance, such as whipped cream or beaten egg whites, into another substance without releasing air bubbles. Cut down through mixture with spoon, whisk, or fork; go across bottom of bowl, up and over, close to surface. The process is repeated while slowing rotating the bowl until the ingredients are thoroughly blended

FRICASSEE: To cook by braising; usually applied to fowl or rabbit

FRY: To cook in hot fat. To cook in a fat is called pan frying or sautéing; to cook in a one- to two-inch layer of hot fat is called shallow-fat frying; to cook in a deep layer of hot fat is called deep-fat frying

GARNISH: To decorate a dish both to enhance its appearance and to provide a flavorful contrast. Parsley, lemon slices, raw vegetables, chopped chives, and other herbs are all forms of garnishes

GLAZE: To cook with a thin sugar syrup cooked to crack stage; mixture may be thickened slightly to cover with a thin, glossy icing

GRATE: To rub on a grater that separates the food in various sizes of bits or shreds

GRATIN: From the French word for crust. Term used to describe any oven-baked dish—usually cooked in a shallow, oval gratin dish—on which a golden brown crust of breadcrumbs, cheese, or creamy sauce is formed

GREASE: To rub the inside of a baking dish or pan with shortening, butter, or oil, or to coat with cooking spray to keep the contents from sticking

GRILL: To cook on a grill over intense heat

GRIND: To process solids by hand or mechanically to reduce them to tiny particles

HULL: To remove the green stems and leaves of strawberries

HUSK: To remove the outer leaves from an ear of corn

INDIRECT HEAT: To cook foods on a grill over a drip pan with the coals placed on one or both sides of the drip pan. This process is used to cook larger cuts of meat or less tender cuts

JULIENNE: To cut vegetables, fruits, or cheeses into thin strips

KNEAD: To work and press dough with the palms of the hands or mechanically, to develop the gluten in the flour

LINE: To cover a baking sheet with parchment paper, wax paper, or foil to prevent sticking

LUKEWARM: Neither cool nor warm; approximately body temperature

MARINATE: To flavor and moisturize pieces of meat, poultry, seafood, or vegetables by soaking them in or brushing them with a liquid mixture of seasonings known as a marinade. Dry marinade mixtures composed of salt, pepper, herbs, or spices may also be rubbed into meat, poultry, or seafood

MEUNIÈRE: Dredged with flour and sautéed in butter

MINCE: To cut or chop food into extremely small pieces

MIX: To combine ingredients usually by stirring

PAN BROIL: To cook uncovered in a hot fry pan, pouring off fat as it accumulates

PANFRY: To cook in small amounts of fat

PARBOIL: To boil until partially cooked; to blanch. Usually this procedure is followed by final cooking in a seasoned sauce

PARE: To remove the outermost skin of a fruit or vegetable

PEEL: To remove the peels from vegetables or fruits

PICKLE: To preserve meats, vegetables, and fruits in brine

PINCH: A pinch is the trifling amount you can hold between your thumb and forefinger

PIT: To remove pits from fruits

PLANKED: Cooked on a thick, hardwood plank

PLUMP: To soak dried fruits in liquid until they swell

POACH: To cook very gently in hot liquid kept just below the boiling point

PROCESS: To combine, blend, chop, or puree foods in a food processor or blender

PREHEAT: To bring an oven up to the baking temperature before baking

PULSE: To process foods in a food processor or in a blender with short bursts of power. This is accomplished by quickly turning the machine off and on

PUREE: To mash foods until perfectly smooth by hand, by rubbing through a sieve or food mill, or by whirling in a blender or food processor

REDUCE: To boil down to reduce the volume

REFRESH: To run cold water over food that has been parboiled, in order to stop the cooking process quickly

RENDER: To make solid fat into liquid by melting it slowly

ROAST: To cook by dry heat in an oven

ROUX: A French term for a mixture of flour and fat that is cooked together until brown and used to thicken gumbos, soups, and sauces

SAUTE: To cook and/or brown food in a small amount of hot fat

SCALD: To bring to a temperature just below the boiling point

SCALLOP: To bake a food, usually in a casserole, with sauce or other liquid. Crumbs often are sprinkled over

SCORE: To cut narrow grooves or gashes partway through the outer surface of food

SEED: To remove seeds from fruits and vegetables

SEAR: To brown very quickly by intense heat. This method increases shrinkage but develops flavor and improves appearance

SHRED: To cut or tear in small, long, narrow pieces

SHUCK: To remove the meat of oysters and clams from their shells. Also refers to removing the husk from an ear of corn

SIFT: To put one or more dry ingredients through a sieve or sifter

SIMMER: To cook slowly in liquid over low heat at a temperature of about 180°F. The surface of the liquid should be barely moving, broken from time to time by slowly rising bubbles

SKIM: To remove impurities, whether scum or fat, from the surface of a liquid during cooking, thereby resulting in a clear, cleaner-tasting final product

SNIP: To cut herbs into small pieces using kitchen shears

STEAM: To cook in steam in a pressure cooker, deep well cooker, double boiler, or a steamer made by fitting a rack in a kettle with a tight cover. A small amount of boiling water is used, more water being added during steaming process, if necessary

STEEP: To extract color, flavor, or other qualities from a substance by leaving it in water just below the boiling point

STERILIZE: To destroy microorganisms by boiling, dry heat, or steam

STEW: To simmer slowly in a small amount of liquid for a long time

STIR: To mix ingredients with a circular motion until well blended or of uniform consistency

STOCK: A long-simmered broth made from meat, poultry, fish, and/or vegetables with herbs and spices

STRAIN: To separate solids from liquid by pouring through a sieve or colander

STUFF: To fill the cavity of fish, poultry, or pork chops with a bread, rice, vegetable, fruit, or nut mixture

TEAR: To use your hands to pull apart into evenly sized pieces, such as when tearing salad leaves

THREAD: To place pieces of meat and vegetables onto skewers as when making kabobs

TOSS: To combine ingredients with a lifting motion

TRUSS: To secure poultry with string or skewers, to hold its shape while cooking

WARM: To hold foods at a low temperature, usually around 200°F, without further cooking

WHIP: To beat rapidly to incorporate air and produce expansion, as in heavy cream or egg whites

WHISK: A multi-looped, wire mixing utensil with a handle used to whip sauces, eggs, cream, etc., to a smooth, airy consistency. Also means to whip ingredients together

ZEST: To finely grate the peel of a citrus fruit, such as a lemon, lime, or orange

MEASURING UTENSILS FOR COOKING

Graduated Nested Measuring Cups

- These measuring cups range in size from ¼ cup to 1 cup; some sets contain ⅛ cup (2 tablespoons), ⅔ cup, and ¾ cup measures, as well. Use these to measure dry ingredients and solid fats, such as shortening.

- For flour, baking mixes, and sugar, spoon ingredient lightly into cup, then level with a straight-edged spatula or knife. Sift powdered sugar only if lumpy.

- For cereal or dry breadcrumbs, pour into cup. Level with a straight-edged spatula or knife.

- For shredded cheese, chopped nuts, coconut, and soft breadcrumbs, spoon into cup and pack down lightly.

- For solid fats and brown sugar, spoon into cup and pack down firmly with a spatula or spoon.

Graduated Measuring Spoons

- These measuring spoons range in size from ¼ teaspoon to 1 tablespoon; some sets contain ⅛ teaspoon up to ¾ teaspoon.

- Use spoons to measure liquids and dry ingredients.

- For thin liquids, pour into spoon until full.

- For thick liquids and dry ingredients, pour or scoop into spoon until full, then level with a straight- edged spatula or knife.

Glass Measuring Cups

- Glass cups can be purchased in 1, 2, 4, and 8-cup sizes. Use to measure liquids.

- For an accurate amount, always read the measurement at eye level while the cup is placed on a flat surface.

- To measure sticky ingredients, such as honey, molasses, or corn syrup, first coat the cup lightly with oil so the liquid will be easier to remove.

WEIGHTS AND MEASUREMENTS [4]

Teaspoon and Tablespoon Measurements

Dash or Pinch=less than ⅛ teaspoon

1½ teaspoons=½ tablespoon

3 teaspoons=1 tablespoon; ½ fluid ounce

4½ teaspoons=1½ tablespoons

2 tablespoons=⅛ cup; 1 fluid ounce

4 tablespoons=¼ cup; 2 fluid ounces

8 tablespoons=½ cup; 4 fluid ounces

12 tablespoons=¾ cup; 6 fluid ounces

16 tablespoons=1 cup; 8 fluid ounces; ½ pint

Cup, Tablespoon, Ounce and Pint Measurements

⅛ cup=2 tablespoons; 1 fluid ounce

¼ cup=4 tablespoons; 2 fluid ounces

⅓ cup=5⅓ tablespoons

½ cup=8 tablespoons; 4 fluid ounces

⅔ cup=10⅔ tablespoons

¾ cup=12 tablespoons; 6 fluid ounces

⅞ cup=¾ cup plus 2 tablespoons

1 cup=16 tablespoons; 8 fluid ounces; ½ pint

2 cups=1 pint; 16 fluid ounces

4 cups=2 pints; 1 quart; 32 fluid ounces

Pint, Quart, Gallon, and Pound Measurements

½ pint=1 cup; 8 fluid ounces

1 pint=2 cups; 16 fluid ounces

1 quart=4 cups; 32 fluid ounces

1 gallon=4 quarts; 16 cups

¼ pound=4 ounces

½ pound=8 ounces

¾ pound=12 ounces

1 pound=16 ounces

[4] *The Taste of Home Cookbook* (Reiman Media Group Inc., 2009).

Conversion Cheat Sheet

QUICK AND EASY KITCHEN EQUIVALENTS

16 Tablespoons = 1 Cup

2 Cups = 1 Pint

4 Cups = 1 Quart

3 Teaspoons = 1 Tablespoon

2 Tablespoons = 1 Fluid Ounce

4 Tablespoons = 1/4 Cup

8 Tablespoons = 1/2 Cup

4 Quarts = 1 Gallon

HELPFUL HINTS FOR COOKING [5]

- Use a small amount of oil when preparing sauces and marinades for red meats. Fat from the meat will provide plenty of juice and flavor. Certain meats, like ribs, pot roast, sausage, and others can be parboiled (boil until partially cooked) before grilling to reduce the fat content, or trim fat from meat with a sharp knife.

- When shopping for red meats, buy the leanest cut you can find. Fat will show up as an opaque white coating or can also run through the meat fibers, as marbling. Although most of the fat (the white coating) can be trimmed away, there is not much that can be done about the marbling. The more marbling there is within a cut of beef, the more oleic acid, which means less of the potentially harmful saturated and trans-fatty acids that have given beef a black eye. Oleic acid is a simple (monounsaturated) fat prevalent in olive oil.

- Home from work late with no time to marinate meat? Pound the meat lightly with a mallet or rolling pin, pierce with a fork, sprinkle lightly with meat tenderizer, and add marinade. Refrigerate for about twenty minutes, and you will have succulent, tender meat.

- Marinating is a cinch if you use a plastic zipper-lock bag. The meat stays in the marinade and is easy to turn and evenly coat. Cleanup is easy as well; just toss the bag. Can be left in the refrigerator for up to twenty-four hours.

- Partially frozen meat slices better. Example: Slicing sausage patties, polish, or kielbasa sausage.

- Tomatoes added to a roast will naturally help to tenderize the meat. Tomatoes contain an acid that works well to break down the meat.

- Whenever possible, cut meats across the grain; they will be much easier to eat and have a better appearance.

- When frying meat, sprinkle paprika over it to turn it a golden brown color.

- Thaw all meats in the refrigerator for maximum safety.

- Refrigerate poultry immediately after purchasing. Keep in coldest part of refrigerator for up to two days. Freeze poultry for longer storage. Never leave raw poultry at room temperature for more than two hours.

[5] *A Collection of Favorite Recipes by Cherry House Furniture Galleries* (Cookbooks by Morris Press, 2001).

No-Bake Cookies

1 cup peanut butter, crunchy or smooth

½ cup milk

½ teaspoon salt

1 teaspoon vanilla

3½ cups old-fashioned or quick rolled oats

½ cup unsalted butter, softened

¼ cup cocoa powder

2 cups sugar

1 teaspoon cinnamon

1 cup semisweet chocolate chips or peanut butter chips

Cover cookie sheets with wax paper or parchment paper. Measure out peanut butter into a bowl. In a saucepan melt the butter; add cocoa, sugar, and milk. Stir over medium heat and bring to a boil. Remove from heat, pour over peanut butter and mix well. Add vanilla. Stir until smooth. Add oats and cinnamon, stirring until completely combined. The dough will seem sticky and moist, but it thickens as it cools. Drop by teaspoon onto greased or parchment paper-lined cookie sheet. Place semisweet chocolate or peanut butter chips on top. Chill. Note: For peanut allergy, substitute almond butter for peanut butter.

Blueberry Crumble

2 cups all-purpose flour

¾ cup sugar

½ cup milk

¼ cup butter

1 egg, room temperature

2 teaspoons baking powder

½ teaspoon salt

½ teaspoon nutmeg

1 cup frozen blueberries

Preheat oven to 375°F. Grease and flour a square baking pan. Combine all the cake ingredients except blueberries in mixing bowl. Beat at low speed until well mixed. Gently fold in blueberries by hand. Spread batter into pan. Streusel: ½ cup sugar, ½ cup all-purpose flour, 1 teaspoon cinnamon, ½ teaspoon nutmeg and ¼ cup butter softened. Place all ingredients into bowl except butter. Cut in butter with pastry cutter or fork until coarse crumbles form. Sprinkle over batter. Bake for 40 to 45 minutes until golden brown.

SARAH
A Woman Unwilling to Wait

Biblical Principle: God will act on behalf of those who are willing to wait on Him. See Isaiah 64:4.

Read Genesis Chapters 12, 15, 16, 17, and 21.

1. What does God promise Abraham?

2. Is he willing to wait on God?

3. Sarah has a promise from God even though she is barren; is she willing to wait on God?

4. What does she do in her barrenness? What does she see as her only solution?

5. Can God always be trusted to keep His promise? Why are we unwilling to wait?

6. Abraham and Sarah were unwilling to wait on God, so they made a mess of things. Has there been a time in your life when you were unwilling to wait on God? What happened as a result?

7. Prayerfully consider the following:

   If God says, WAIT on Me for the right college, are you willing to wait?
   If God says, WAIT on Me for a husband, are you willing to wait?
   If God says, WAIT on Me for a house, are you willing to wait?
   If God says, WAIT on Me for a baby, are you willing to wait?
   If God says, WAIT on Me for a job, are you willing to wait?
   If God says, WAIT on Me for healing, are you willing to wait?

8. What lessons have you learned from Sarah that you can apply to your own life?

What I Learned Today

Week Four

TIPS ON PLANNING MEALS

HOT DOGS AND BEAN WITH BACON SOUP

Mark and I married in 1973 at the ages of twenty-two and seventeen. The day after our wedding, we left Nashville, Tennessee, for South Florida, where Mark was working. I would imagine about now you are asking, what could a seventeen-year-old girl have known about marriage or homemaking. Not much! My grocery shopping and meal-planning experience, in particular, were at a minimum. Like most teenagers, I had run to the store for my mom, but as far as planning meals and doing the main grocery shopping, I was inexperienced! Week after week, we would go to the grocery store. Yes, I said we. When we were first married, Mark enjoyed going, and, after all, we couldn't be apart! I truly believe we spent twice as much. When it came to meal planning that first year of marriage, hot dogs and bean with bacon soup were my specialties. That was about as creative as it got. Sounds good, huh?

I have learned over the years that if I plan our meals for the week, my grocery shopping is much easier, and I save money buying only what I will need that week. But girls, let's face it, grocery shopping is not much fun and can often be very frustrating, especially if you go without a list or a plan in mind. Have you ever walked into the grocery store without a list knowing there were things you needed, but you just couldn't remember what they were? Have you ever walked in the door and thought to yourself, Now, why am I here, and what is it I need? When that is the case, what usually happens is that you get home to find you just purchased your third bottle of mustard, but you forgot the detergent you have needed for a week.

When we are prepared and have planned ahead, it takes the frustration out of grocery shopping. Well, some of the frustration! Speaking of frustration, years ago I was checking out in a local grocery store; that particular week, I had a great deal of coupons—back in the day when you cut your coupons from the newspaper and magazines. I got in line with my cart loaded down with groceries and only twenty minutes to get checked out and to the school to pick up the girls. Of all the days to get a new checker! He was a cocky, young teenager who was not at all happy about my coupons. I wasn't even what they call an "extreme couponer." Basically, I used coupons for cereal, cleaners, paper products, and a few other regularly purchased items. I handed the young man the stack of coupons, and he proceeded to ask me if I had purchased all these items. I tried not to get offended that he was questioning my integrity and graciously answered, yes. He waited until all the items had been scanned and bagged, then looked at me and said he would have to check to see that I had purchased all the items.

The grocery industry has made great strides since then; now the computer will refuse a coupon if you have not purchased the product. But back then, it was up to the checker to make sure you had purchased every item. He went bag by bag—my twenty minutes were totally used up! I was becoming more and more upset. In the end, I had purchased everything for which I had handed him a coupon. I left never wanting to step foot in a grocery store again; but then that would not be possible, would it? Because your family enjoys eating, you must go to the grocery store, like it or not.

So, here we go ... like it or not!

MEAL PLANNING

Just the words *Meal Planning* incite terror and panic in some of us. To many, the thought of planning an entire week's worth of menus is a daunting task. I have researched many different meal planning methods and found each suited the woman writing about her plan. At that point, it dawned on me that the key to meal planning is finding the method that suits you! Meal planning is a really personal thing. What works for you may not work for me. The goal, I think, is to find a process that is both enjoyable, effective, and one that works for your family.

Meal planning is whatever way you organize yourself to cook a meal, whether it is breakfast, lunch, or dinner. It is the plan you make before you grocery shop. Some people plan a month in advance, freezing neatly-labeled packets of soup and casseroles. And others wing it shopping for that evening's meal picking up whatever looks good to them. I like to plan a week at a time, due to an ever changing schedule. You will have to decide what method works best for you.

Meal planning has a multitude of benefits. One very important benefit is that it will actually reduce your stress. For me standing in the kitchen at 5 o'clock and trying to decide what to prepare for dinner is very stressful. Having a plan in place for the week relieves that daily stress. Who wants more stress? So, let's get started ...

REASONS TO MEAL PLAN:

- Healthier

- Cost efficient

- Relieves stress

WHERE TO START:

- **PLAN:** Find a time that works best for you to plan your menus and do your grocery shopping. Putting those days on your calendar each week will help you stay on track. I would suggest planning one day and shopping the next.

- **METHOD:** Whether you use a piece of notebook paper or print a meal planning chart from a website is up to you. The key is to have your plan in writing as a guide for the upcoming week's meals. Establishing a routine for planning and shopping will help you remain consistent with your meal planning method.

- **COLLECT RECIPES:** If you are not using a source such as Real Plans, begin to collect recipes that your family will enjoy and are suited to your way of eating, e.g., Paleo, Vegetarian, Dairy-free, etc. The number of resources for recipes are vast: Pinterest, The Pioneer Woman, Allrecipes, Genius Kitchen, Food Network, Wellness Mama, Menuboard, etc.

- **CHOOSE RECIPES:** Include in your weekly planning those faithful recipes that your family loves (the ones you know by heart), and add one or two new recipes each week. Choose the number of meals you will be preparing based on your family's schedule that week. Make out your grocery list according to your recipes.

- **GROCERY LIST:** Look in your pantry before going to the store to see if you already have on hand some of the ingredients called for in your recipes and eliminate those items from your list. Once that is complete, make a list of the ingredients you will need to prepare each recipe and organize your grocery list by the section of the store where the food items are found.

- **LEFTOVERS:** Choose recipes that will bless you with leftovers! You might say they are the gift that keeps on giving.

- **PRODUCE:** Always place recipes requiring fresh produce at the beginning of the week. You do not want to waste money by having your produce go bad.

- **WEBSITE:** Overwhelmed at the thought of stepping out on your own? Use a website such as Realplans.com. This site creates a custom plan to suit your family's size, busy schedule, and ever-changing needs. There is a monthly fee, but it might be worth it for those who just do not have the time to plan or are working outside the home.

- **OPTIONAL:** Organize recipes by season: Produce is fresher, easier to find and less expensive when in season. It is easier to plan around foods that are readily available. This method adds variety to your menu and keeps everyone from getting bored with the same recipes. Start with the season you are currently in and build your collection of different recipes for each season as you go.

- I think you are ready! Happy shopping!

STEPS FOR PREPARING A MEAL:

- **WORK AHEAD:** Prepping is the key to taking the stress out of preparing a meal. If you plan on Friday and shop on Saturday, you might consider prepping your vegetables and meat on Sunday afternoon. Any prep you can do ahead of time will be a great help during the week.

- **MEAT PREP:** If time allows, once home from the grocery store, according to your recipes for the week, prep your meat, e.g., brown the ground beef, make hamburger patties, tenderize and season the chicken breast, flour and braise your roast, etc. Once cooled, all of your meat preps can be wrapped thoroughly and stored in the freezer until needed.

- **PREPPING TAKES TIME:** Think ahead about dinner and utilize every spare minute to prepare meat and vegetables. Examples: If your children are older and can dress themselves for school, take a few minutes to wash and wrap the baked potatoes for dinner while they are dressing. If your children are small, you could prep while they are eating breakfast, playing, or napping. Utilize those snippets of time to get some of your prep work done.

- **SAVE TIME:** Example: If a chopped onion is called for in two of your recipes this week, dice an entire onion and store half for later in the week. Perhaps you are having carrots as a side on Monday and carrots in a casserole dish later in the week. As you are preparing the carrots earlier in the week, go ahead and peel and cut the remaining carrots for later. Store them in an air-tight plastic bag or in shallow bowl of water in the refrigerator.

- **EQUIPMENT:** Having the right equipment or tools on hand saves time. Example: Use a small food processor to chop onion and garlic. You will save time and energy!

- **BUSY NIGHT:** Prepare an easy meal, serve a make ahead frozen casserole, put a meal in the crockpot that morning, or use an Instant Pot®.

- **PLANS CHANGE:** No problem. When this happens, just switch meals. Because you have all your ingredients on hand, it is easy to switch out meals.

- **USE LEFTOVERS:** Leftovers are great for breakfast or lunch. Example: Roasted veggies could go in an omelet. Your children could take dinner leftovers in insulated containers for school lunches. Be creative!

- **FREEZING IS KEY TO PREPPING AHEAD.** We will talk about freezing tips in Week Five.

 WEEKLY MEAL PLAN WEEK OF _____

Breakfast   Lunch   Dinner

	Breakfast	Lunch	Dinner
MONDAY			
TUESDAY			
WEDNESDAY			
THURSDAY			
FRIDAY			
SATURDAY			
SUNDAY			

Shopping List

PRODUCE

- [ ] _____
- [ ] _____
- [ ] _____
- [ ] _____
- [ ] _____

DAIRY

- [ ] _____
- [ ] _____
- [ ] _____
- [ ] _____
- [ ] _____

MEATS

- [ ] _____
- [ ] _____
- [ ] _____
- [ ] _____
- [ ] _____

BREAD/CEREAL

- [ ] _____
- [ ] _____
- [ ] _____
- [ ] _____

CANNED GOODS

- [ ] _____
- [ ] _____
- [ ] _____
- [ ] _____

BAKING/SPICES

- [ ] _____
- [ ] _____
- [ ] _____
- [ ] _____

CONDIMENTS

- [ ] _____
- [ ] _____
- [ ] _____

OTHER

- [ ] _____
- [ ] _____
- [ ] _____

- [ ] _____
- [ ] _____
- [ ] _____

STATISTICS ON *Family Meal Times* [6]

Girls, did you know there are actually statistics that show the value of having family meals around a table? We live in a busy society, and many families eat on the go, the kitchen table replaced by drive-thru, fast-food restaurants. In an article written by Dr. Bill Bellican, he stated, "More than a decade of research conducted by the National Center of Addiction and Substance Abuse (CASA) at Columbia University has consistently found that benefits accrue the more often children have dinner with their parents. These benefits include children/teenagers being less likely to smoke, drink, or use drugs." Simply summarized: family dinners make a difference.

Among the research findings are that teens who have infrequent family dinners, fewer than three per week, as compared to teens who have frequent family dinners, five to seven per week, are:

- Twice as likely to use tobacco or marijuana and are more likely to use alcohol

- More likely to report getting lower grades in school

- More likely to have friends who drink regularly and use marijuana or other illegal drugs or misuse prescription drugs

- Twice as likely to say they will try drugs in the future

- More likely to think their father is okay with them drinking

- More likely to say they have fair or poor relationships with their parents

- More likely to say it is hard to talk to their parents about personal things

- Less likely to attend religious services, which correlates to increased likelihood of smoking, drinking, and drug use.

Dr. Bellican concluded the article by saying, "The once-in-a-while dinner meal around the table needs to be made routine. God knew that the family needed this type of interaction during mealtime to foster communication, togetherness, bonding and intimacy. To borrow from a familiar Bible verse, 'Therefore what God has joined together (at the dinner table), let man not separate because of busyness, distractions, texting, cell phones, and too many activities.'" Matthew 19:6

Girls, let's get back to the basics. God made families to need one another. Dinnertime is vital to your children's well-being and the future of your family. Slow down and bond around the table. Say no to all the distractions, the busyness, and get to know each other! No more fast-food family dinner moments!

RECOMMENDED BOOKS:

- *The Hour that Matters Most* by Les and Leslie Parrott, with Stephanie Allen and Tina Kaun

- *One Year Dinner Devotionals* by Nancy Guthrie

- *The Family Dinner (e-book)* by Laurie David

- *Let's Eat* by Dianne Dougharty and Secrets Savored Ministry

[6] Dr. Bill Bellican, "The Family Meal: For the Holidays ... Or Every Day?," *Mid-South Families*, no.3 (November 2010).

QUICK AND EASY MEALS

Pan Gravy

2 tablespoons drippings (fat and juices)

2 to 3 tablespoons flour

1 cup liquid (meat juices, broth, or milk)

Salt and pepper to taste

Use drippings from cooked meat with any brown particles. Place in skillet and blend in flour with wire whisk. Cook over low heat, stirring until mixture is smooth and bubbly. Turn to very low heat, or remove from heat and add liquid gradually. Stir constantly to keep lumps from forming. Heat gravy to a boil while continuing to stir. Season to taste with salt and pepper. Gravy may be thickened or thinned as needed. To thicken, add additional flour. To thin, add additional liquid.

Thin White Sauce

1 tablespoon butter

1 to 2 tablespoons flour

¼ teaspoon salt

⅛ teaspoon pepper

1 cup milk or half and half

Melt butter in small saucepan over low heat. Stir in flour, salt, and pepper. Cook over low heat, stirring until butter and flour are smooth and bubbly. Add milk gradually while stirring constantly. Boil 1 minute. <u>Note:</u> For Medium-thick White Sauce, double flour and butter.

Slaw Salad with Chicken

1 cup oil

⅓ cup apple cider vinegar

½ cup sugar

2 (3 ounce) packages beef ramen noodles

1 (16 ounce) bag coleslaw mix

1 bunch green onions, chopped

1 cup salted sunflower seeds

1 cup sliced almonds, toasted

1½ cups roasted chicken, chopped

Mix oil, vinegar, sugar, and flavor packets from ramen noodles. Refrigerate dressing overnight. In a large bowl, combine coleslaw mix, onion, sunflower seeds, and almonds. Just before serving, shake and pour dressing over coleslaw mixture. Add chicken, toss to mix. Break up ramen noodles and sprinkle over salad. <u>Note:</u> Ramen beef packages have MSG. If you are wanting a healthier version, Whole Foods® and other health food stores often carry an organic ramen. If beef flavor packet is not included in healthier version, use MSG free bouillon or ¼ cup organic beef broth in the dressing.

Chicken Pizza with Alfredo Sauce

SAUCE: ENOUGH FOR TWO TO THREE PIZZAS

4 tablespoons butter

4 tablespoons all-purpose flour

¼ teaspoon salt

1 dash of black pepper or for a little kick, red pepper flakes

1 cup milk

¾ cup Romano cheese, grated

SUGGESTED TOPPINGS:

1 tablespoon fresh, chopped basil or 1 to 2 teaspoons dried leaf basil or fresh spinach leaves

Sliced ripe olives

Green onion, chopped

Grape tomatoes, sliced

6 to 8 ounces cooked chicken, cut up in chunks

1½ cups Mozzarella cheese, shredded

Preheat oven to 400°F. Bake Pillsbury®classic pizza dough for five minutes at 400°F. Remove from oven and cool. In saucepan over medium heat, melt butter. Add flour, salt, and pepper and whisk until blended. Slowly add milk and mix well. Cook two minutes until thickened. Remove from heat; add Romano and mix until melted. Spread onto pizza crust, and then add additional ingredients. Bake for 20 to 25 minutes until golden brown. Note: Pillsbury® pizza crust is found in dairy section of store. For leftover sauce, use on top of vegetables or pour over pasta.

Oriental Chicken Cashew Salad

1 head lettuce, any variety

1 (14 ounce) can mandarin oranges, drained

1 (8 to 9 ounce) can cashews

1 small can of thin chow mein noodles

1½ cups roasted chicken, cut in chunks

1 (16 ounce) bottle Kraft Asian dressing

1 (8 ounce) can water chestnuts, drained and chopped

Wash and drain lettuce. Chop and place in bowl. Drain oranges and water chestnuts, place on top of lettuce along with cashews and Chow Mein noodles. Top with chicken chunks. Drizzle with your favorite Asian dressing.

Tortilla Soup

1 small onion, chopped

3 cloves garlic, minced

1 teaspoon cumin

3 tablespoons vegetable oil

2 tablespoons Liquid Smoke

1 (8 ounce) can whole kernel corn, drained

1 (28 ounce) can whole tomatoes, pureed

3 (14 ounce) cans chicken broth

½ bunch cilantro, chopped, plus extra for topping

Chopped jalapeño peppers to taste

3 cups cooked and cubed chicken breasts/roasted chicken

Fresh tortilla chips and shredded cheese for topping

In large soup pot, sauté onions, garlic, and cumin in a small amount of oil until tender. Add liquid smoke, corn, pureed tomatoes, broth, cilantro, and jalapeño peppers. Add chicken to soup and simmer 20 minutes. Top individual servings with tortilla chips, cheese, and a sprinkle of cilantro. <u>Note</u>: Additional Tortilla Soup recipe in Week Eight.

Chicken Wild Rice Soup

5 ⅔ cups water

1 (4.3 ounce) package long grain and wild rice mix

1 (2¼ ounce) package chicken noodle soup mix

1 stalk celery, chopped

1 medium carrot, chopped

⅓ cup onion, chopped

2 (10¾ ounce) cans cream of chicken soup

1 cup cooked chicken, cubed

In a large saucepan, combine water, rice mix with seasoning package, and soup mix. Bring to a boil. Reduce heat, cover, and simmer 10 minutes. Stir in celery, carrot, and onion. Cover and simmer 10 minutes. Stir in cream of chicken soup and chicken. Cook 8 minutes longer or until rice and vegetables are tender.

Mile High Potatoes

4 large baking potatoes

Olive oil for coating

Sea salt for coating

2 tablespoons butter, melted

1 medium red or green pepper, chopped

1 small onion, chopped

4 tablespoons taco seasoning

1½ cups cooked chicken breast, shredded

1 cup sharp Cheddar cheese, shredded

½ cup Monterey Jack cheese, shredded

1 small can ripe black olives, drained

2 tablespoons diced green chilies

1 cup salsa

Guacamole, optional

Sour cream, optional

Preheat oven to 400°F. Scrub potatoes, dry, coat with olive oil and sea salt, wrap in foil. Place in oven and bake for 1-1½ hours. In a medium saucepan, cook pepper and onion in butter until tender. Add taco mix. Cook one minute, stirring constantly; remove from heat. Stir in chicken, cheeses, olives, and chilies. Slice potato lengthwise and fill with chicken mixture. Top with salsa, guacamole, and sour cream. Note: Add black beans, chopped tomatoes, and chopped jalapeño for a Mexican potato. Substitute a chopped roasted chicken for cooked shredded chicken breast.

Making Sour Cream

Sour Cream: Using unpasteurized heavy cream, add 1 tablespoon vinegar to 2 cups heavy cream. Let stand at room temperature for several hours until curdled.

Crème Fraîche: This is a milder form of sour cream. Take 1 cup buttermilk and add 2 cups heavy cream. Leave at room temperature (80 to 90°F). Let stand for as few as twenty-four hours and as long as forty-eight hours, until curdled. Can be whipped.

Kelly's Flank Steak Sandwiches with Caramelized Onions

¼ cup olive oil

2 tablespoons sugar

2 medium onions, sliced

Salt and pepper to taste

Flank or skirt steaks, medium size

Package hoagie buns, 4 to 6

1 cup mayonnaise

¼ cup sundried tomatoes

2 tablespoons fresh thyme, chopped

Place olive oil in large skillet, heat over medium heat, add sugar, and stir. Add sliced onions and cook for 20 to 25 minutes, stirring often. Cook onions until tender and dark golden brown. Salt and pepper flank steak and place on hot grill, cook 3 to 4 minutes on each side. Remove and cover with foil for 5 to 10 minutes. Remove foil and thinly slice steak. Place on buttered and grilled hoagie buns, top with caramelized onions. Mix mayo, sundried tomatoes, and thyme in a bowl, spread on bun and enjoy! Note: Adding shredded Pepper Jack cheese is another option in place of the mayonnaise mixture. This combination creates a spicy and sweet sandwich all in one. Serve with chips or your favorite pasta salad.

Honey-Glazed Chicken Breast

¼ cup raw honey

¼ cup low-sodium soy sauce

⅓ cup onion, chopped

2 tablespoons fresh ginger, grated

2 garlic cloves, minced

4 chicken breasts, bone-in/skin-on

2 tablespoons olive oil

2 teaspoons paprika

Preheat oven to 375°F. Combine first five ingredients in a large zipper-lock bag; add chicken. Seal bag and chill for 2 hours, turn occasionally. Remove chicken from bag. Place chicken breasts face down on a cooling rack on top of a cookie sheet. Pour sauce over breast. Bake covered with aluminum foil for 20 minutes. Uncover chicken breasts, baste with olive oil, and sprinkle with paprika. Bake uncovered for 10-15 minutes or until cooked through. Remove from oven and let stand for 10 minutes. Serve with hot brown rice and salad. Note: A ½ teaspoon of ground ginger can be substituted for the 2 tablespoons of fresh ginger.

Chicken Enchiladas

1 dozen flour tortillas

1½ cups Monterrey Jack cheese, shredded

1½ cups Rotisserie chicken, finely shredded

½ cup onion, minced

1 (4 ounce) package cream cheese, room temperature

2 tablespoons Southwestern spice blend (any Mexican spice blend)

TOPPING:

¼ cup butter, melted

¼ cup flour, for thickening

2 cups chicken broth

½ cup sour cream

Salt and pepper to taste

Preheat oven to 425°F. In mixing bowl, place cheese (reserving ½ cup for topping), shredded chicken, minced onion, cream cheese, and seasoning. Mix thoroughly. Place a scoop of chicken mixture in each tortilla, spread and roll up. Place in buttered 9x13 baking dish. In saucepan melt butter over medium heat. Add flour and whisk to incorporate. Slowly add chicken broth and stir until creamy. Remove from stove and stir in sour cream and salt and pepper to taste. Pour sauce over enchiladas and top with remaining cheese. Bake for 20 minutes until heated through and golden brown.

HAGAR
A Woman of Submission

Biblical Principle: Submitting to God's authority in our lives enables us to submit to others in places of authority.

Read Genesis Chapter 16.

1. Who was Hagar?

2. What did Sarah ask of her? What were the results?

3. Hagar ran away, and then God came to her and told her to return to her mistress. What was Hagar's response?

4. Are you completely surrendered to whatever God has for you? Tell of a time when you responded in obedience to God's desire for surrender in a specific area of your life and the results.

5. Hagar was a woman who submitted (surrendered) to what God asked of her. Prayerfully consider: Is there any area of your life that is not submitted (surrendered) to your Heavenly Father? Explain…

   Prayerfully bring this area of your life to God in submission.

6. What have you learned from Hagar that you can apply to your life?

What I Learned Today

Week Five

COOKING BASICS

IT'S THEIR BREAD

*M*y son-in-law has a nickname for me—The Freezer Queen. Apparently, when he was growing up, his mother froze very little. Since he entered our family, he has been amazed at all the things that I freeze. Just about everything goes in the freezer at some point. Shortly after our first grandchild was born, I was at my daughter and son-in-law's home. I was cleaning the kitchen when a loaf of bread on top of the refrigerator caught my eye. My first thought was, That is going to dry out if it is left up there. So, what did I do? Of course, I did the logical thing; I put it in the freezer to preserve it.

That evening, once I arrived home, my cell rang, and I heard, "Mom, what did you do with our loaf of bread?" If she had known me as well as I thought she did, she would have known the answer to that question! It was in the freezer, naturally. I told her that I was concerned it would dry out. My daughter let me know kindly, but in no uncertain terms, that they did not put their bread in the freezer.

---

*M*other-in-Law 101—do not put their bread that they bought in their freezer when you are at their house cleaning and caring for their baby! Seriously, I did learn a valuable lesson. I was in their home, and their bread was none of my concern. I was not there to preserve their bread, but to be a help to my daughter and care for the baby. Oh, and did I say, clean their house?

Over the years, I have been amazed at how fascinated women are with the idea of freezing. Believe it or not, I have been asked several times to do a freezing talk and demonstration. Some women at our church are called upon to speak because of their deep insight into God's Word. They have been sought after to speak on topics such as prayer, disciple making, and mentoring. Not me, I am the freezing expert. I am still looking for the spiritual value in a freezing talk! God's Word does tell us to use our gifts; so if it is freezing, then tell others about freezing!

MEAT PREPARATION FOR SAVING TIME

- For Chicken or Fish: Once arriving home from the grocery store, separate meat into serving sizes, place in large zipper-lock bags, cover with marinade, then freeze. When needing an entrée for dinner, remove from the freezer and thaw in the refrigerator for the day or in a water bath for that evening. Meat marinates as it thaws. <u>Note</u>: Also works well with beef and pork.

- When hamburgers are on the menu for the week, once you are home from the grocery store, go ahead and make up the patties. Wrap each individual patty and place in a large zipper-lock bag and freeze until needed. Hamburgers are juicier when going from freezer to grill and cooked on low to medium heat.

- Meats can be pan seared and frozen to use later, such as chicken and many cuts of beef, roasts, chopped steak, etc.

- Try cooking whole chicken breasts (bone-in and skin on) using a Reynolds Oven Bag. Place chicken breasts into bag. Top with ¼ cup chopped onions, salt and pepper, and 2 tablespoons garlic powder. Seal the bag, pierce and bake at 325°F for 2 hours; meat will be juicy. If chicken breasts are frozen, bake for 3 hours. The meat will fall off the bone. Good for soups and casseroles.

- Take chicken breasts, a meat mallet, two one-gallon size zipper-lock bags, and a bottle of your favorite marinade. Demonstrate tenderizing the chicken breast by placing them in one bag and using a meat mallet to tenderize. In second bag, pour in your marinade, place boneless chicken breasts in bag, and make sure each one is coated with marinade. Place in freezer. They can be thawed in refrigerator or in cool water bath, and it will marinate as it thaws. Grill or bake.

- For boneless skinless chicken breast, place chicken breast in dish, drizzle with olive oil, and sprinkle with Cavenders All-Purpose Greek Seasoning.® Bake at 350°F for 30 to 40 minutes until done. <u>Note</u>: Chicken needs either an oil or fat from skin to stay moist. Once chicken is cooked, it can be frozen for later use in soups, casseroles, etc.

- Good marinades: Caber Brothers, Newman's Italian dressing, Lawry's seasonings, Fuddruckers Restaurant seasoning, and Herb's Meats All-Purpose Seasoning (herbsmeats.com), or use any vinaigrette salad dressing. Be creative; make your own.

Defrosting Guidelines
USING THE REFRIGERATOR

- For ½ to ¾-inch thick ground beef or veal patties, allow at least 12 hours for thawing.

- For 1 to 1½-inch thick meat pieces or packages of ground beef and veal, allow at least 24 hours for thawing.

- For steaks, allow 12 to 24 hours to thaw.

- For a large roast or a thick pot roast, allow 6 hours per pound.

- The thicker the package, the larger the amount of meat, the longer it will take to defrost.

USDA FACTS ON FREEZING AND FOOD SAFETY [7]

Foods in the freezer—are they safe?

Every year, thousands of callers to the USDA Meat and Poultry Hotline aren't sure about the safety of items stored in their own home freezers. The confusion seems to be based on the fact that few people understand how freezing protects food. Here is some information on how to freeze food safely and how long to keep it.

WHAT CAN YOU FREEZE?

You can freeze almost any food. Some exceptions are canned foods or eggs in shells. However, once the food (such as a ham) is out of the can, you may freeze it.

Being able to freeze food and being pleased with the quality after defrosting are two different things. Some foods simply don't freeze well. Examples are mayonnaise, cream sauces, and lettuce. Raw meat and poultry maintain their quality longer than their cooked counterparts because moisture is lost during cooking.

IS FROZEN FOOD SAFE?

Food stored constantly at 0°F will always be safe. Only the quality suffers with lengthy freezer storage. Freezing keeps food safe by slowing the movement of molecules, causing microbes to enter a dormant stage. Freezing preserves food for extended periods because it prevents the growth of microorganisms that cause both food spoilage and food-borne illnesses.

[7] USDA, "Fact Sheets, Safe Food Handling, Freezing and Food Safety" http://www.fsis.usda.gov/FactSheets/Focus_On_Freezing/index. asp This information is sponsored by the U.S. Department of Agriculture, Food Safety and Inspection Service.

DOES FREEZING DESTROY BACTERIA AND PARASITES?

Freezing to 0°F inactivates any microbes, bacteria, yeasts, and molds present in food. Once thawed, however, these microbes can again become active, multiplying under the right conditions to levels that can lead to food-borne illnesses. Since they will then grow at about the same rate as trichina and other parasites, they can be destroyed by subzero freezing temperatures. However, very strict government-supervised conditions must be met. It is not recommended to rely on home freezing to destroy trichina. Thorough cooking will destroy all parasites.

FRESHNESS AND QUALITY

Freshness and quality at the time of freezing affect the condition of frozen foods. If frozen at peak quality, foods emerge tasting better than foods frozen near the end of their useful life. So freeze items you won't use quickly, sooner rather than later. Store all foods at 0° or lower to retain vitamin content, color, flavor, and texture.

NUTRIENT RETENTION

The freezing process itself does not destroy nutrients. In meat and poultry products, there is little change in nutrient value during freezer storage.

ENZYMES

Enzyme activity can lead to the deterioration of food quality. Enzymes present in animals, vegetables, and fruit promote chemical reactions, such as ripening. Freezing only slows the enzyme activity that takes place in foods. It does not halt these reactions, which continue after harvesting. Enzyme activity does not harm frozen meats or fish and is neutralized by the acids in frozen fruits. But most vegetables that freeze well have low acidity and require a brief, partial cooking to prevent deterioration. This is called "blanching." For successful freezing, blanch or partially cook vegetables in boiling water or in a microwave oven. Then rapidly chill the vegetables prior to freezing and storage. Consult a cookbook for timing.

PACKAGING

Proper packaging helps maintain quality and prevents "freezer burn." **It is safe to freeze meat or poultry directly in its supermarket wrapping,** but this type of wrap is permeable to air. Unless you will be using the food in a month or two, over wrap these packages as you would any food for long-term storage using airtight, heavy-duty foil, freezer plastic wrap, freezer paper, or place the package inside a freezer plastic bag. Use these materials or airtight freezer containers to repackage family packs into smaller amounts. It is not necessary to rinse meat and poultry before freezing. Freeze unopened vacuum packages as is. If you notice that a package has accidentally been torn or has opened while food is in the freezer, the food is still safe to use; merely over wrap or rewrap it.

FREEZER BURN

Freezer burn does not make food unsafe, merely dry in spots. It appears as grayish-brown leathery spots and is caused by air reaching the surface of the food. Cut freezer-burned portions away either before or after cooking the food. Heavily freezer-burned foods may have to be discarded for quality reasons.

COLOR CHANGES

Color changes can occur in frozen foods. The bright red color of meat as purchased usually turns dark or pale brown depending on its variety. This may be due to lack of oxygen, freezer burn, or abnormally long storage.

Freezing doesn't usually cause color changes in poultry. However, the bones and the meat near them can become dark. Bone darkening results when pigment seeps through the porous bones of young poultry into the surrounding tissues when the poultry meat is frozen and thawed. The dulling of color in frozen vegetables and cooked foods is usually the result of excessive drying due to improper packaging or over-lengthy storage.

FREEZE RAPIDLY

Freeze food as fast as possible to maintain its quality. Rapid freezing prevents undesirable large ice crystals from forming throughout the product because the molecules don't have time to take their positions in the characteristic six-sided snowflake. Slow freezing creates large, disruptive ice crystals. During thawing, they damage the cells and dissolve emulsions. This causes meat to "drip"—lose juiciness. Emulsions such as mayonnaise or cream will separate and appear curdled.

Ideally, food two inches thick should freeze completely in about two hours. If your home freezer has a "quick-freeze" shelf, use it. Never stack packages to be frozen. Instead, spread them out in one layer on various shelves, stacking them only after frozen solid.

REFRIGERATOR-FREEZERS

If a refrigerator freezing compartment cannot maintain zero degrees or if the door is opened frequently, use it for short-term food storage. Eat those foods as soon as possible for best quality. Use a freestanding freezer set at 0°F or below for long-term storage of frozen foods. Keep a thermometer in your freezing compartment or freezer to check the temperature. This is important if you experience a power outage or mechanical problems.

LENGTH OF TIME

Due to the fact that freezing keeps food safe almost indefinitely, recommended storage times are for quality only. Refer to the freezer storage chart at the end of this article, which lists optimum freezing times for best quality.

If a food is not listed on the chart, you may determine its quality after defrosting. First, check the odor. Some foods will develop a rancid or "off" odor when frozen too long and should be discarded. Some may not look picture perfect or be of high enough quality to serve alone but may be edible; use them to make soups or stews. Cook raw food and if you like the taste and texture, use it.

SAFE DEFROSTING

Do not defrost foods in a garage, basement, car, dishwasher, plastic garbage bag, out on the kitchen counter, outdoors, or on the porch. These methods can leave your foods unsafe to eat.

There are three safe ways to defrost food: in the refrigerator, in cold water, or in the microwave. It's best to plan ahead for slow, safe thawing in the refrigerator. Small items may defrost overnight, most foods require a day or two, and large items like turkeys may take longer—approximately one day for each five pounds of weight.

For faster defrosting, place food in a leak-proof plastic bag and immerse it in cold water. (If the bag leaks, bacteria from the air or surrounding environment could be introduced into the food. Tissues can also absorb water like a sponge, resulting in a watery product.) Check the water frequently to be sure it stays cold. Change the water every thirty minutes. After thawing, cook immediately.

When microwave-defrosting food, plan to cook it immediately after thawing because some areas of the food may become warm and begin to cook during microwaving.

REFREEZING

If the food item is thawed in the refrigerator, it is safe to refreeze it without cooking, although there may be a loss of quality due to the moisture lost through defrosting. After cooking raw foods that were previously frozen, it is safe to freeze the cooked foods. If previously cooked foods are thawed in the refrigerator, you may refreeze the unused portion.

If you purchase previously frozen meat, poultry, or fish at a retail store, you can refreeze if it has been handled properly.

COOKING FROZEN FOODS

Raw or cooked meat, poultry, or casseroles, can be cooked or reheated from the frozen state. Add an additional thirty minutes of cooking time to the usual cooking time for meats and casseroles. Remember to discard any wrapping or absorbent paper from meat or poultry.

When cooking whole poultry, remove the giblet pack from the cavity as soon as you can loosen it. Cook the giblets separately. Read the label on USDA-inspected frozen meat and poultry products. Some, such as pre-stuffed whole birds, **MUST** be cooked from the frozen state to ensure a safely cooked product.

Look for the USDA or state mark of inspection.

The inspection mark on the packaging tells you the product was prepared in a USDA or state-inspected plant under controlled conditions. Follow the package directions for thawing, reheating, and storing.

POWER OUTAGE IN FREEZER

If there is a power outage, the freezer fails, or if the freezer door has been left ajar by mistake, the food may still be safe to use. As long as a freezer with its door ajar is continuing to cool, the foods should stay safe overnight. If a repairman is on the way or if it appears the power will be on soon, just don't open the freezer door.

A freezer full of food will usually keep about two days if the door is kept shut; a half-full freezer will last about a day. The freezing compartment in a refrigerator may not keep foods frozen as long. If the freezer is not full, quickly group packages together so they will retain the cold more effectively. Separate meat and poultry items from other foods so if they begin to thaw, their juices won't drip onto other foods. When the power is off, you may want to put dry ice, block ice, or bags of ice in the freezer or transfer foods to a friend's freezer until power is restored. Use an appliance thermometer to monitor the temperature.

When it is freezing outside and there is snow on the ground, it seems like a good place to keep food until the power comes on; however, frozen food can thaw if it is exposed to the sun's rays, even when the temperature is very cold. Refrigerated food may become too warm and food-borne bacteria could grow. The outside temperature could vary hour by hour and the temperature outside will not protect refrigerated and frozen food. Additionally, perishable items could be exposed to unsanitary conditions or to animals. Animals may harbor bacteria or disease; never consume food that has come in contact with an animal.

To determine the safety of foods when the power goes on, check their condition and temperature. If food is partly frozen, still has ice crystals, or is as cold as if it were in a refrigerator (40°F), it is safe to refreeze or use. It's not necessary to cook raw foods before refreezing. **Discard foods that have been warmer than 40°F for more than two hours. Discard any foods that have been contaminated by raw meat juices.** Dispose of soft or melted ice cream for quality's sake.

FROZEN CANS

Accidentally frozen cans, such as those left in a car or basement in subzero temperatures, can present health problems. If the cans are merely swollen—and you are sure the swelling was caused by freezing—the cans may still be usable. Let the can thaw in the refrigerator before opening. If the product doesn't look and/or smell normal, throw it out. DO NOT TASTE IT! If the seams have rusted or burst, throw the cans out immediately, wrapping the burst can in plastic and disposing the food where no one, including animals, can get it.

FROZEN EGGS

Eggs in their shell should not be frozen. In the case where a whole egg is frozen in the shell and remains without cracks, keep frozen until needed; then thaw in the refrigerator. It can be hard cooked successfully but other uses may be limited. That's because freezing causes the yolk to become thick and syrupy so it will not flow like an unfrozen yolk or blend very well with the egg white or other ingredients.

Freezer Storage Chart* (32°F=0°C)

<u>Note</u>: Freezer storage is for quality only. Frozen foods remain safe indefinitely.

ITEM	MONTHS
Bacon and Sausage	1 to 2
Casseroles	2 to 3
Egg Whites or Egg Substitutes	12
Frozen Dinners and Entrees	3 to 4
Gravy, meat or poultry	2 to 3
Ham, Hotdogs, and Lunchmeats	1 to 2
Meat, uncooked roasts	4 to 12
Meat, uncooked steaks or chops	4 to 12
Meat, uncooked ground	3 to 4
Meat, cooked	2 to 3
Poultry, uncooked whole	12
Poultry, uncooked parts	9
Poultry, uncooked giblets	3 to 4
Poultry, cooked	4
Soups and Stews	2 to 3
Wild game, uncooked	8 to 12

HELPFUL HINTS

- When preparing a casserole, make an additional one to freeze. It makes a great emergency meal when unexpected guests arrive. Just take the casserole from the freezer and bake in the oven adding an additional thirty minutes to baking time.

- To keep hot oil from splattering, sprinkle a little salt or flour in the pan before frying.

- Don't refreeze cooked, thawed foods unless thawed in the refrigerator.

- A few drops of lemon juice added to simmering rice will keep the grains separated.

- Clove, garlic, and pepper flavors get stronger when they are frozen. Sage, onion, and salt get milder.

- For an easy, no-mess side dish, grill vegetables in oven while cooking meat.

- When freezing foods, label each container with its contents and the date it was put in the freezer. Always use frozen cooked foods within one to two months for better freshness.

- Always refrigerate brown rice and refrigerate or freeze grains if they will not be used within five months.

- A little vinegar or lemon juice added to potatoes before draining will make them extra white when mashed.

- To quickly bake potatoes, place them in boiling water for 10 to 15 minutes. Pierce their skins with a fork and bake in a preheated oven.

- For healthier entrees and side dishes, use cooking methods that require little to no fat. Roasting, broiling, grilling, sautéing, stir-frying, poaching, and steaming are great ways to cook meats and vegetables using a small amount of fat.

- For healthier dishes, choose leaner cuts of meat and trim visible fat from meat.

- When preparing cheesy casseroles, creamy soups, or rich sauces, consider using the lighter version of the ingredients called for in the recipe.

- Rely on fresh or frozen vegetables rather than canned, which have higher sodium levels.

  As stated before, there are three methods to thaw frozen foods:

1. Refrigerator, cold water, and microwave. The safest is the refrigerator, because if your plans change, the meat or vegetable dish can remain in refrigerator up to four days before using and can also be refrozen. This method takes longer.

2. The cold water is time consuming; water needs to be changed every thirty minutes and meat must be cooked. For larger items, you should estimate a defrost time of thirty minutes per pound of food in cold water.

3. Microwave thawing is the faster choice. Set your microwave to defrost or 50% power

setting while thawing. Watch to make sure outer edges of the food do not become cooked while the center remains frozen. Food will need to be cooked immediately; it can be frozen once cooked.

- Instead of topping meats and vegetables with gravies or cheesy sauces, season with flavorful herbs, spices, or condiments. Try dry herb rubs and tangy fruit salsas on grilled meats and lemon juice and fresh herbs on steamed vegetables. <u>Note</u>: Strawberry Salsa, Peach Kiwi Salsa, and Rub recipe below:

Strawberry Salsa

1 cup strawberries, sliced

½ cup onions, finely chopped

1 tablespoon jalapeño pepper, finely chopped

1 tablespoon fresh cilantro, minced

1 teaspoon lime rind, grated

1 tablespoon fresh lime juice

Combine all six ingredients in a medium bowl to make salsa. Chill for an hour before topping grilled fish or chicken.

Peach Kiwi Salsa

2 fresh peaches, peeled, pitted, coarsely chopped

1 kiwi fruit, peeled, coarsely chopped

2 tablespoons green onions, thinly sliced

2 tablespoons parsley, chopped

1 tablespoon lime juice

¼ teaspoon crushed red pepper

Combine all the salsa ingredients in a small bowl. Cover; chill in refrigerator for at least one hour. Serve as a topping for grilled fish or chicken.

Jerk Rub for Steak

4 green onions, coarsely chopped

1 garlic clove

1 jalapeño pepper, seeded

1 tablespoon ground allspice

1 teaspoon dried thyme

½ teaspoon ground nutmeg

½ teaspoon ground red pepper

2 tablespoons lime juice

In food processor or blender process until smooth, stopping to scrape down sides. Rub evenly on steaks, cover and chill for 6-8 hours. Grill steaks, with grill lid down over medium-high heat for 6 to 7 minutes on each side until desired doneness.

EASY RECIPES

Brewed Sweet Tea

2 cups cold water

8 regular tea bags

1 cup sugar

Water

Bring cold water to a rapid boil. Remove from heat and add tea bags. Allow tea to steep for 10 minutes. Remove tea bags, squeeze out excess liquid, and throw away. Add sugar and stir until dissolved. Pour into pitcher and add enough water to make 2 quarts. Refrigerate until chilled.

Variation: For a decidedly refreshing change in flavor, add one flavored tea bag such as peach, blackberry, vanilla, etc.

Grilled Chicken Pasta with Roasted Vegetables and Pesto

4 skinless boneless chicken breasts

Salt and pepper to taste

Italian seasoning to taste

2 yellow squash, cut into 1-inch slices

2 zucchini, cut into 1-inch slices

1 crown broccoli, cut, stems removed

2 tablespoons olive oil

1 (1 pound) box Fettuccini pasta

½ red onion, thinly sliced

1 (6 ounce) jar pesto

1½ cup Parmesan cheese, grated, reserve ½ cup for topping dish

Preheat oven to 400°F. Sprinkle chicken with salt, pepper, and a little Italian seasoning. Place on hot grill, cook for about 8 minutes on each side. Remove from grill and set aside to cool. Chop and place vegetables in a zipper-lock bag with olive oil. Make sure all of the vegetables are coated, and then pour out onto a cookie sheet. Separate the vegetables for even cooking. Place cookie sheet in oven and roast vegetables for 20 to 25 minutes, stirring twice during roasting time; cook until golden brown and tender. Cook pasta according to the package directions. Drain pasta, reserving ¼ cup of the pasta water. Place pasta in a large bowl. Cut the chicken breast into bite-sized pieces and toss along with the vegetables into the pasta. Add ¼ cup pasta water, jar of pesto and 1 cup Parmesan cheese; stir to thoroughly mix. Salt and pepper to taste. Top with grated Parmesan and serve. Serve with salad. <u>Note</u>: The roasted vegetables will cook faster when sliced thin.

Tuscan Salad

2 cups fresh green beans, cut into 1 to 2-inch pieces

1 head Romaine lettuce, torn

1 (15 ounce) can Cannellini beans, drained

½ cup Parmesan, grated

1 teaspoon Kosher salt

1 teaspoon ground black pepper

1 lemon, juiced

¼ cup Extra Virgin olive oil

Optional: ½ red onion, cut into slivers

Optional: ½ cup black olives, drained

Bring a medium pot of salted water to a boil over high heat. Add the green beans and stir. Cook for about 2 minutes, or until beans are slightly tender. Transfer the cooked green beans to a bowl of ice water and let cool for 3 minutes. Drain the green beans. In a large bowl, combine the green beans with the lettuce, cannellini beans, (olives and red onion, if desired). Toss to combine. Drizzle with lemon juice and olive oil. Sprinkle with salt and pepper and toss to coat. Top with grated Parmesan and serve. Note: Store-bought vinaigrette dressing can be substituted for lemon dressing.

Strawberry Trifle Cake

1 quart fresh strawberries, sliced

1 (5.25 ounce) package instant vanilla pudding mix, prepared according to package directions, chilled

1 angel food cake, (boxed mix or store bought)

1 (8 ounce) container of whipped topping or fresh whipped cream

Rinse and remove caps from strawberries, reserving three or four for the top of the finished dessert. Slice berries and set aside. Break up cooled angel food cake into fairly large chunks. Place a layer of cake chunks into a trifle bowl or any deep bowl, preferably clear so you can see the layers. Spoon a layer of pudding over the cake pieces. Cover with one-third of the strawberries. Repeat process two more times. Cover last layer with whipped topping. Add reserved whole strawberries for garnishing the top. Trifle is best when refrigerated for a couple of hours before serving. Optional: Add a sprinkle of chopped pecans to topping for decoration.

Homestyle Pot Roast

¼ cup flour

1 Reynolds Oven Bag

⅔ cup water

1 envelope onion soup mix

3 to 3½ pounds boneless beef chuck pot roast

6 to 8 small, whole red potatoes

1 medium onion, quartered

1 (1 pound) bag carrots, peeled and sliced

2 to 3 tablespoons parsley, chopped

Preheat oven to 325°F. Place flour in oven bag and shake. Add water and soup mix and squeeze bag to mix together. Place flour in oven bag and shake. Place bag with roast into a 9x13 casserole dish. Add potatoes, onion, and carrots into the bag around roast. Close oven bag, cut six small slits in top and place in oven. Bake for 3 hours until roast is tender. Sprinkle with parsley and serve.

Easy Chicken Parmesan

4 boneless chicken breast halves

2 tablespoons garlic powder

2 tablespoons oregano

Salt and pepper to taste

½ stick butter, melted

½ cup butter crackers, crushed

¾ cup Parmesan cheese, grated

Preheat oven to 350°F. Season chicken breasts with garlic powder, oregano, salt, and pepper. Place in a covered dish and refrigerate for at least one hour. Remove chicken and dip into melted butter, then dip in a mixture of cracker crumbs and Parmesan cheese. Bake for 20 to 30 minutes. Optional: Top with favorite Marinara sauce.

Chicken Wrapped in Bacon

6 boneless chicken breast

6 slices of bacon

½ bottle Italian dressing

Salt and pepper to taste

1 (8 ounce) package sliced Monterey Jack cheese

Preheat oven to 350°F. Wrap each chicken breast with a slice of bacon. Place in a lightly greased baking dish, salt and pepper. Pour Italian dressing over chicken and marinate in refrigerator for 3 hours. Remove bacon-wrapped chicken from marinade and place in a clean dish. Bake for 40 minutes. Remove from oven and top with cheese. Return to oven for 2 to 3 minutes until cheese is melted. Serve hot.

Easy BBQ Quesadillas

2 cups cooked chicken, chopped

1 (15 ounce) can black beans, drained and rinsed

½ cup BBQ sauce

4 (10 inch) flour tortillas or burritos

1 cup plum tomatoes, seeded and diced

2 green onions, finely chopped

2 cups Mexican style or Colby Jack cheese, shredded

2 tablespoons butter, melted

Toppings: Avocado, mashed and sour cream

Garnish: fresh cilantro

Preheat oven to 400°F. In a large mixing bowl, stir together chicken, beans, and BBQ sauce. Place tortilla in a lightly greased 10-inch spring form pan and spread with meat mixture. Sprinkle with each tomato, green onion, and cheese. Repeat layers twice. Top with remaining tortilla, spread top with melted butter. Gently press and cover with foil. Bake for 20-30 minutes till golden brown. Remove sides of pan and slice in triangles. Top with avocado, sour cream, and fresh cilantro.

SOUPS

White Bean Chicken Chili

1 medium onion, diced

1 tablespoon olive oil

3 (15 ounce) cans Northern beans, drained

3 to 4 chicken breasts, cooked and diced

6 cups low-sodium chicken broth

2 (4 ounce) cans chopped chilies

2 cloves garlic, minced

1½ teaspoons dried oregano

2 teaspoons cumin

¼ teaspoon cayenne pepper

1½ cups Monterey Jack cheese, shredded

In a large pot, sauté onion in olive oil until tender. Add remaining ingredients with the exception of the cheese. Simmer for 50 to 60 minutes. Five minutes before serving, add cheese and stir until melted. Serve hot.

Easy Potato Cheese Soup

4 tablespoons butter

1 cup chicken broth

1 teaspoon garlic powder

⅛ teaspoon onion powder

¼ teaspoon pepper

1 teaspoon cornstarch or flour

2 tablespoons water

2 (10¾ ounce) cans potato soup

1 (15 ounce) can evaporated milk

¾ to 1 cup milk for desired thickness

1½ cups Cheddar cheese, shredded

Combine butter, chicken broth, onion powder, garlic powder, and pepper in large pot. Bring to a boil. Dissolve the cornstarch in 2 tablespoons water and stir into boiling liquid. Add potato soup, evaporated milk, and milk. Mix well. Simmer for 30 minutes. Five minutes before serving, add cheese and stir until melted. Serve hot.

Quick Vegetable Soup

1 (8 ounce) can tomato sauce

1 (10 ounce) package frozen mixed vegetables

2 cups water

4 teaspoons low-sodium beef bouillon or 4 cups beef broth

1 (14.5 ounce) can chopped tomatoes

Salt and pepper to taste

Combine all ingredients in a Dutch over or large pot. Bring to a boil. Cover, reduce heat, and simmer for 30 minutes, stirring occasionally. **Vegetable Beef Soup:** Brown 1 pound ground chuck in a large skillet, stirring until crumbled and no longer pink. Drain. Add to soup and simmer.

Eating Healthier:
MAKING HEALTHY MEALS [8]

My mother-in-law was a home economics teacher for years. I heard her say on numerous occasions that if we would just eat according to the Food Pyramid, we would not have an obesity problem. My mom, on the other hand, believed that if we limited our calorie intake, we would not have an obesity problem. Both women believed in limited portions and both were small, petite, and healthy, as they entered into midlife and beyond. Most young women have never seen a Food Pyramid or a calorie counter. I was a member of Weight Watchers and worked there for a year and a half. What I found was that people are ignorant as to how to lower the fat and calories of their food. We are not teaching people how to trim down fat, calories, or portions, and because of that, we have an abundance of obesity in the United States.

You may have family-favorite recipes that you no longer prepare because they are higher in fat, cholesterol, sodium, and sugar. Using the tips below, you can still enjoy those family favorites, if you take the time to make them healthier.

LOWERING CHOLESTEROL

To reduce cholesterol, limit foods that are higher in saturated fats, such as butter and shortening. Use monounsaturated fats such as safflower oil, olive oil, canola oil, or polyunsaturated fats such as sunflower oil, soybean, and corn oil. Research is showing that the use of coconut oil has great health benefits as well. Butter-flavored spray may also be used.

Cholesterol can also be reduced by limiting the number of egg yolks in recipes. In breakfast recipes and baked goods, replace whole eggs with egg whites or egg substitute. Two egg whites or ¼ cup egg substitute are equal to one whole egg. It is best for the quality of a recipe to leave at least one whole egg in the recipe.

CUTTING FAT

For your entrees and many side dishes, use cooking methods that add little to no fat. Roasting, grilling, broiling, sautéing, stir-fry, poaching, and steaming are good ways to cook meats and vegetables using small amounts of fat or none at all.

Choose leaner cuts of meat. (Google "lean cuts of meat" to see a recommended list) Trim all visible signs of fat. Roast, broil, or grill meat on a rack allowing fat to drip off during cooking. Remove and discard all skin from chicken or turkey after cooking. Use dry herbs and tangy fruit salsas on grilled meats and lemon juice and fresh herbs on vegetables in place of heavy gravies, creams, and sauces.

For casseroles calling for cheese and sour cream, try using reduced-fat sour cream, shredded cheese, and cream soup. Fat-free half and half can be used in place of half and half cream. For dips, spreads, and salad dressings, use the fat-free or reduced-fat varieties of sour cream, cream cheese, mayonnaise, and cottage cheese. Plain yogurt can be substituted for sour cream.

In baked goods, applesauce can be used as a fat substitute as well as pureed pears, peaches, apricots, plums, baby food fruit puree, or mashed bananas. Try replacing half the butter, margarine, shortening or oil with a fat substitute.

[8] Dr. David Katz, *The Way to Eat* (Naperville, IL: Sourcebooks, Inc., 2002).

If the recipe calls for ½ cup butter, use ¼ cup butter and ¼ cup puree. To cut fat in desserts, use the reduced-fat whipped topping, reduced-fat graham crackers crusts, fat-free yogurt, and fat-free ice cream toppings.

CUTTING SODIUM

Canned vegetables can be very high in sodium. Use fresh or frozen vegetables to lower sodium intake. Use reduced-sodium broths, soups, and soy sauce. Instead of seasoning with salt, use flavored vinegars, citrus juices, salt-free seasoning blends, and fresh or dried herbs and spices.

REDUCING SUGAR

When making baked goods, start by simply reducing the amount of sugar by 25 percent. When reducing it 50 percent, add a sugar replacement to make up for the other half. Splenda Sugar Blend for Baking is a very good substitute. To reduce the amount of sugar in other dessert recipes, consider using the sugar-free versions of products like gelatin and instant pudding, and replace jams with reduced-sugar jam and fruit spreads. Instead of topping cakes or brownies with canned frosting, sprinkle with a little confectioners' sugar. To enhance taste when using less sugar, use spices like cinnamon, cardamom, allspice, nutmeg, and mace. Also, consider extracts, such as vanilla and almond, to add more flavor.

HEALTHIER EATING: ADD OMEGA-3 FATS WITH:

Salmon, tuna, herring, mackerel, and halibut

Flaxseed and wheat germ

Walnuts, hazelnuts, pecans, and almonds (recommended by the National Diabetes Foundation)

Variety of beans

HEALTHIER EATING: INCREASE FIBER WITH:

Crunchy vegetables

Trail mix with unsalted nuts and unsulfured dried fruits

Whole grain pastas and breads

Bean dishes

Freshly ground flaxseed, nuts and seeds, dried fruit, and beans (add to salads and smoothies)

Brown rice

Mega fiber muffins, pancakes, and cookies

Veggie burgers/Turkey burgers

Berries (add to morning cereal)

DR. DAVID KATZ SAYS:

1. Never trust the front of the package; read the ingredient list.

2. The first ingredient listed is always the greatest quantity within the product.

3. Harmful ingredients: hydrogenated oils, artificial color (red, yellow, caramel color, or artificial flavors), nitrates and nitrite, artificial sweeteners, preservatives, BHA, BHT, EDTA, etc., MSG—monosodium glutamate, hydrolyzed vegetable protein, autolyzed yeast, potassium bromated, sulfites—sulfur dioxide and others, sodium nitrate—in hot dogs and deli meats, and sodium benzoate or benzoic acid. Suggestion: Make a chart with above ingredient list, laminate, and keep in purse when grocery shopping.

Note: Since this article was released in 2002, a great deal of research has been done on the use of low-fat and non-fat foods. Many researchers believe that additives in these products such as sugar substitutes and sodium are more unhealthy than eating smaller amounts of foods in their natural state. An example would be choosing real butter over a butter substitute or margarine. A great deal of research has also been done on the effects of highly saturated oils in our diet. In years past, Canola oil was believed to be the healthy choice (and it is healthier than Crisco or vegetable oil), but now nutritionist are recommending oils such as Olive oil, Coconut oil, and Walnut oil. Do your research and make the adjustments needed according to your own dietary needs.

HOW TO READ
A NUTRITION FOOD LABEL [9]

Start here ◉

Check the total calories per serving ◉

Limit these nutrients ◉

Get enough of these nutrients ◉

Quick Guide to % Daily Value: 5% or less is low 20% or more is high ◉

Nutrition Facts

Serving Size 1 slice (47g)
Servings Per Container 6

Amount Per Serving

		% Daily Value*
Calories 160	Calories from Fat 90	
Total Fat 10g		15%
Saturated Fat 2.5g		11%
Trans Fat 2g		
Cholesterol 0mg		0%
Sodium 300mg		12%
Total Carb 15g		5%
Dietary Fiber less than 1g		3%
Sugars 1g		
Protein 3g		
Vitamin A 0%	Vitamin C 4%	
Calcium 45%	Iron 6%	
Thiamin 8%	Riboflavin 6%	
Niacin 6%		

*Percent Daily Values are based on a 2,000 calorie diet. Your daily values may be higher or lower depending on your calorie needs.

START HERE. Note the size of a single serving and how many servings are in the package.

CHECK TOTAL CALORIES PER SERVING. Look at the serving size and how many servings you're really consuming. If you double the servings you eat, you double the calories and nutrients, including the Percent Daily Value (% DV).

LIMIT THESE NUTRIENTS. Remember, you need to limit your total fat to no more than 56–78 grams a day—including no more than 16 grams of saturated fat, less than two grams of trans fat, and less than 300 *mg* cholesterol (for a 2,000 calorie diet).

GET ENOUGH OF THESE NUTRIENTS. Make sure you get 100 percent of the fiber, vitamins, and other nutrients you need every day.

QUICK GUIDE TO % DV. The % DV section tells you the percent of each nutrient in a single serving, in terms of the daily recommended amount. As a guide, if you want to consume less of a nutrient (such as saturated fat, cholesterol, or sodium), choose foods with a lower % DV—5 percent or less is low. If you want

[9] American Heart Association, "Food Labels" http://www.heart.org/HEARTORG/GettingHealthy/NutritionCenter/ Nutrition-Center_UCM_001188_SubHomePage.jsp Compliments of the American Heart Association and the U.S. Food and Drug Administration.

to consume more of a nutrient (such as fiber), seek foods with a higher % DV—20 percent or more is high.

Here are more tips for getting as much health information as possible from the Nutrition Facts label:

- Remember that the information shown in these panels is based on 2,000 calories a day. You may need to consume less or more than 2,000 calories depending upon your age, gender, activity level, and whether you're trying to lose, gain, or maintain your weight. Find out your personal daily limits on My Fats Translator at americanheart.org.

- In general, as you think about the amount of calories in a food per serving, remember that for a 2,000-calorie diet:

  1. 40 calories per serving is considered low;

  2. 100 calories per serving is considered moderate; and

  3. 400 calories or more per serving is considered high.

- There is no % DV shown for *trans* fat on the panel because the U.S. Food and Drug Administration (FDA) does not have enough scientific information to set this value. We recommend eating less than 20 calories or (less than two grams of *trans* fat) a day—that's less than 1 percent of your total daily calories (for a 2,000-calorie-a-day diet).

- When the Nutrition Facts panel says the food contains "0 g" of *trans* fat, it means the food contains less than 0.5 grams of *trans* fat **per serving**.

- When the Nutrition Facts label says a food contains "0 g" of *trans* fat, but includes "partially hydrogenated oil" in the ingredient list, it means the food contains *trans* fat, but less than 0.5 grams of *trans* fat per serving. So, if you eat more than one serving, you could quickly reach your daily limit of *trans* fat.

In addition to the Nutrition Facts label, a lot of foods today also come with nutrient content claims provided by the manufacturer. These claims are typically featured in ads for the foods or in the promotional copy on the food packages themselves. They are strictly defined by the FDA. The chart* below provides some of the most commonly used nutrient content claims, along with a detailed description of what the claim means.

If a food claims to be...	It means that one serving of the product contains...
Calorie free	Less than 5 calories
Sugar free	Less than 0.5 grams of sugar

Fat	
Fat free	Less than 0.5 grams of fat
Low fat	3 grams of fat or less
Fat	

Reduced fat or less fat	At least 25 percent less fat than the regular product
Low in saturated fat	1 gram of saturated fat or less, with not more than 15 percent of the calories coming from saturated fat
Lean	Less than 10 grams of fat, 4.5 grams of saturated fat and 95 milligrams of cholesterol
Extra lean	Less than 5 grams of fat, 2 grams of saturated fat and 95 milligrams of cholesterol
Light (lite)	At least one-third fewer calories or no more than half the fat of the regular product, or no more than half the sodium of the regular product

Cholesterol	
Cholesterol free	Less than 2 milligrams of cholesterol and 2 grams (or less) of saturated fat
Low cholesterol	20 or fewer milligrams of cholesterol and 2 grams or less of saturated fat
Reduced cholesterol	At least 25 percent less cholesterol than the regular product and 2 grams or less of saturated fat

Sodium	
Sodium free or no sodium	Less than 5 milligrams of sodium and no sodium chloride in ingredients
Very low sodium	35 milligrams or less of sodium
Low sodium	140 milligrams or less of sodium
Reduced or less sodium	At least 25 percent less sodium than the regular product

Fiber	
High fiber	5 grams or more of fiber
Good source of fiber	1.5 to 4.9 grams of fiber

If you can't remember the definitions of all of the terms, don't worry. You can use these general guidelines instead:

- "Free" means a food has the least possible amount of the specified nutrient.

- "Very Low" and "Low" mean the food has a little more than foods labeled "Free."

- "Reduced" or "Less" mean the food has 25 percent less of a specific nutrient than the regular version of the food.

REBEKAH
A Woman of Deception

Biblical Principle: When we sin by lying and deceiving others, we will suffer a serious consequence—estrangement from God and those we love.

Read Genesis Chapter 25:19—34 and Chapter 27.

1. Looking back at Sarah, what did Rebekah and Sarah have in common?

2. Liz Curtis Higgs in *Bad Girls of the Bible* refers to Rebekah as, "Becky, a girl gone bad."[10] We see in chapter 25 that Rebekah starts out good—seeking God—but somewhere along the way she goes bad.

3. Where did Rebekah go bad?

4. Lying seems to be a family sin. Abraham lied about Sarah being his sister, and then Isaac repeated the sin with Rebekah. If lying is a generational sin in your family, confess it, and determine with God's help to stop this sin that has plagued your family for generations.

5. Rebekah eavesdropped on Isaac and Esau's conversation. What did she proceed to do as a result of what she heard?

6. What deceptive plan did Rebekah lead her son Jacob to do?

7. Rebekah was a woman of deception, which is a sin. What were the results of her sin?

8. What are the lessons you can take away from Rebekah and apply to your own life?

[10] Liz Curtis Higgs, *Bad Girls of the Bible and What We Learn from Them* (Colorado Springs: Waterbrook Press, 2000). 128

What I Learned Today

Week Six

BAKING BASICS

Introduction

TAPIOCA PUDDING AND BROWNIES

*A*s a child, my family had very little monetarily. My parents were both earning their graduate degrees in order to provide a better future for us. As busy as my mom was, she never neglected to keep our home, or cook and bake for us. Due to the lack of funds and having had four children, eating out at a restaurant wasn't an option. In fact, I do not remember eating out at a restaurant until I was in middle school. We did have a few special treats at our house though. One of my earliest memories was Saturday mornings when my mom would make fresh, hot, homemade donuts and dip them in confectioners' sugar or cinnamon sugar. We got to choose our coating; oh were they good!

Another special treat was a trip to the local A&W Root Beer drive-thru to purchase a gallon of ice-cold root beer. We took it home and Mom would make fresh popcorn on the stove; it slowly popped, kernel by kernel. Once the pan was filled to the brim with fresh popped corn, Mom would cover it in melted margarine. You see, butter was much too expensive. What a treat that was for us! Then there was my favorite *special treat*, which we were able to have on occasion—Mom's homemade brownies. I am talking from scratch! While the brownies were baking, Mom would prepare a saucepan of tapioca pudding. We always knew it was chilled and ready when it got a dark yellow film on the top. Mom would scoop it into individual bowls, topped with Cool Whip, and serve it with a homemade brownie, yum! The Jell-O brand tapioca does not hold a candle to Mom's homemade!

---

*O*ne of my favorite treats as a child was my grandpa Barton's homemade chocolate syrup on top of his homemade vanilla ice cream, all from scratch! We would only get that special treat once or twice a year when my grandparents came to visit. Just talking about these treats makes me want to be a child again. I can just taste them now! Being in the kitchen and creating something others will like is what I have enjoyed doing since I was a young girl.

Just so you know, I am not Ree Drummond or Paula Deen, but I do love to cook and bake. I have found it interesting that of my two daughters, one enjoys cooking and the other daughter enjoys baking. Kelly loves to cook; she is always collecting new recipes. Her most prized possession is her Sudoku knife and her nice thick wood cutting board. Lila, her daughter, gets in on everything her mom is making. Our older daughter, Angela, loves to bake; her children enjoy pulling up a chair to the mixer and making their favorite thing—Poppy Seed bread. It is fun for me to watch them both enjoy these aspects of being a homemaker and mom. They are making memories, just as my mom made for me.

Oh, for some hot brownies and fresh homemade tapioca topped with Cool Whip!

Matchin' and Bakin' Game

BATTER   The stage of beating heavy whipping cream or egg whites so that when the beaters are lifted from the mixture, points stand straight up

DOLLOP   To swirl light and dark batters in a cake. It should not be combined to make one color; there should be two distinct colors

DUST   To pierce food or pastry with the tines of a fork to prevent them from bursting or rising during baking

EXTRACTS   To heat milk or cream over low heat until just before boiling

GARNISH   A small mound of soft food such as whipped cream or whipped topping

KNEAD   To lightly sprinkle with confectioners' sugar, baking cocoa, or flour

MARBLE   The distilled essential oils from plant materials, which dissolve in alcohol. Examples: vanilla and almond

PRICK   An edible accompaniment used to decorate a dish for eye appeal, sometimes to boost flavor

SCALD   A mixture made of flour and a liquid such as milk. It may also include other ingredients such as sugar, butter, oil, eggs, leaveners, and flavorings. Consistency ranges from thick to thin

STIFF PEAKS To work dough by using a pressing and folding action to make it smooth and elastic

For correct answers, see "Glossary of Baking Terms"

Glossary of
BAKING TERMS [11]

BAKE: To cook in an oven surrounded by dry heat. When baking, preheat the oven before placing food in.

BATTER: A mixture made of flour and a liquid such as milk. It may also include other ingredients such as sugar, butter, shortening or oil, eggs, leaveners, and flavorings. Consistency ranges from thin to thick.

BEAT: To rapidly mix with a spoon, fork, wire whisk, or electric mixer.

BLEND: To combine several ingredients with a spoon, electric mixer, blender, or food processor.

CHILL: To cool foods to below room temperature (40°F or less) by placing them in the refrigerator, freezer, or an ice bath.

COBBLER: A fruit dessert with a biscuit topping.

COMBINE: To place several ingredients in a single bowl or container and mix thoroughly.

COOL: To bring the temperature of foods to room temperature (70°F).

CREAM: To beat softened butter, margarine, or shortening alone or with sugar using a spoon or mixer until light and fluffy.

CUT-IN: To break down and distribute cold butter, margarine, or shortening into a flour mixture using a pastry blender or two knives.

DISSOLVE: To stir a solid food with a liquid until none of the solid remains, such as yeast with warm water or gelatin in boiling water.

DOLLOP: A small mound of soft food such as whipped cream or whipped topping.

DOUGH: A thick mixture made of flour and a liquid that is not pourable. It may include ingredients such as sugar, butter, shortening or oils, eggs, leaveners, and flavorings. It may be stiff enough to be worked with by hand.

DUST: To lightly sprinkle with confectioners' sugar, baking cocoa, or flour.

EGG WASH: A mixture of beaten egg, egg yolk, or egg whites plus water, which is brushed over breads, rolls, pastries, or piecrusts before baking. This gives the final baked product a shiny, brown finish.

EXTRACTS: The distilled essential oils from plant materials, which are then dissolved in alcohol. Common examples are vanilla and almond.

FLAVORINGS: Chemical compounds that replicate the flavor of a particular food or plant and do not originate from the plant material. Common examples are maple, banana, and coconut.

---

[11] *The Taste of Home Cookbook* (Reiman Media Group Inc. 2009).

FOLD: A method of mixing to combine light or delicate ingredients such as whipped cream or egg whites with other ingredients without beating. A rubber spatula is used to gently cut down through the ingredients to move the spatula along the bottom of the bowl and bring up part of the batter.

FOOD COLORING: Used to tint foods and is available in liquids, gels, and pastes.

FREEZE: To store foods in the freezer.

GARNISH: An edible accompaniment used to decorate a dish for eye appeal and sometimes to boost flavor.

GREASE: To rub the inside of a baking pan or dish with shortening, oil, or butter to coat in order to keep contents from sticking. Cooking spray may also be used.

GREASE AND FLOUR: To rub the inside of a pan or baking dish with shortening, oil, or butter, and then dust with flour. Remove all excess flour from pan. Cooking spray may also be used.

GRIND: To transform a solid piece of food into much smaller pieces using a food processor, blender, or mortar and pestle.

KNEAD: To work dough by using a pressing and folding action to make it smooth and elastic.

LINE: To cover a baking sheet with a piece of parchment paper, waxed paper, or foil to prevent sticking.

MARBLE: To swirl light and dark batters in a cake, bar cookie, cheesecake, or pie. The batter should not be combined to make one color; there should be two distinct batters after marbling.

MIX: To stir or beat two or more ingredients together with a spoon or a fork until well blended.

MOISTEN: To add enough liquid to dry ingredients, while stirring gently, to make a wet, but not runny mixture. Used most often in preparing muffins.

PINCH: A measurement of less than ⅛ teaspoon.

PIPE: To force a soft mixture such as whipped cream, frosting, or meringue through a pastry bag for a fancy shape or design.

PREHEAT: To bring an oven up to the baking temperature before baking.

PRESS: Called a cookie press. Used to push cookie dough into decorative shapes.

PRICK: To pierce food or pastry with the tines of a fork to prevent them from bursting or rising during baking.

PROCESS: To combine or blend, chop, or puree foods in a food processor or blender.

PUNCH DOWN: To use a fist to deflate risen dough after the first rising.

REFRIGERATE: To place in the refrigerator to chill.

ROUNDED TEASPOON OR TABLESPOON: To place dough in a mound within measuring spoon.

SCALD: To heat milk or cream over low heat until just before boiling. Look for small bubbles around the edge of the pan.

SEPARATE: To remove the egg white from the egg yolk.

SIFT: To pass dry ingredients such as flour or confectioners' sugar through a fine mesh strainer or sifter to remove lumps, add air, and combine other ingredients.

SOFT PEAKS: The stage of beating whipping cream or egg whites so that when the beaters are lifted from the mixture, the points of the peaks curl over.

SOFTEN: To bring margarine, butter, or cream cheese to a soft consistency by keeping at room temperature for a short time.

STIFF PEAKS: The stage of beating heavy whipping cream or egg whites when the beaters are lifted from the mixture and the points stand straight up.

STIR: To blend a combination of ingredients by hand using a spoon, going in a circular motion.

WATER BATH: To place a baking dish containing food, such as custard, in a larger dish. The larger dish is filled with hot or boiling water. The dish of food is then baked in the water bath to promote even cooking.

WHIP: To beat rapidly by hand or with an electric mixer to add air and increased volume.

WHISK: A multi-looped wire utensil with handle used for whipping sauces, eggs, cream, etc. to a smooth, airy consistency. Used to whip ingredients together.

ZEST: Removing the outer skin of a citrus fruit, such as lemon or lime, with a utensil called a zester. Peel is used to add natural flavor to the recipe.

Basic Kitchen Utensils FOR BAKING

WHISK:
Balloon Whisk—Large, medium, and small
Batter Whisk
Flat Whisk

FOR PASTRY:
Fluted Pastry Wheel
Marble Pastry Board
Mesh Sugar Shaker
Nonstick Rolling Mat
Pastry Bag
Pastry Brush Set
Piecrust Shield
Rolling Pin—Maple, marble, or silicone
Stainless-Steel Pastry Scraper

BAKING:
Angel Food Cake Pan
Bundt Pan
Cake Pans—Varied sizes
Cheesecake Pan
Cookie Sheets—Varied sizes
Cooling Racks
Hand-Held Electric Mixer
Mini Offset Stainless-Steel Spatula
Muffin Pans—Varied sizes
Offset Stainless-Steel Icing Spatula
Set of Glass Measuring Cups with Spout for Liquids
Set of Metal Measuring Cups
Set of Metal or Plastic Measuring Spoons
Set of Mixing Bowls—Glass or hard plastic
Set of Rubber Spatulas/Silicone Spatulas—All sizes and shapes
Silicone Baking Mats

SPOONS:
Sturdy Metal Spoons
Wooden Spoons

KNIVES:
One Serrated Knife
Paring Knife—Three-inch or four-inch blade
Set made from high-carbon stainless steel
Zester

COLANDERS AND STRAINERS:
Colander—Plastic or steel
Set of Nested Varying Size Strainers—All in stainless steel, also works well as flour sifter

GRATERS:
Metal grater with Various-Sized Holes
Micro Plane Grater
Micro Plane Ultra-Coarse Grater

TONGS:
Non-Stick Tongs
Silicone Locking Tongs
Stainless Steel Tongs

MISCELLANEOUS:
Blender
Can Opener
Food Processor
Hot Mitts/Pads
Ice Cream Scoop
Kitchen Shears
Kitchen Timer
Paper Towel Holder
Piping Bags-Disposable
Set of Decorating Tips
Set of 100 Percent Cotton Dishcloths
Set of 100 Percent Cotton Towels Sifter
Silicone Basting Brush
Trivets

BASIC BAKEWARE [12]

9-inch x 1½-inch round baking pan (need 2 to 4)

13-inch x 9-inch x 2-inch baking pan and/or dish (3 qt.)

10-inch fluted tube pan

15-inch x 10-inch x 1-inch baking pan (jelly-roll pan)

Baking sheets, without sides, in assorted sizes

9-inch spring form pan

9-inch pie plate

12-cup muffin pan (standard size)

6-ounce custard cups (set of six)

9-inch x 5-inch x 3-inch loaf pan (2)

9-inch x 9-inch x 2-inch and 8-inch x 8-inch x 2-inch square baking dish or pan

10-inch tube pan

11-inch x 7-inch x 2-inch baking pan or dish

9-inch deep-dish pie pan

9-inch fluted tart pan with removable bottom

10-inch spring form pan

5¾ -inch x 3-inch x 2-inch loaf pan (3-4)

Miniature muffin pans

10-inch custard cups (set of six)

8-inch fluted tube pan

If you do not have the following pan	Use this pan instead:
One 9-in. x 5-in. x 3-in. loaf pan	Three 5¾-in. x 3-in. x 2-in. loaf pans
One 8-in. x 4-in. by 2-in. loaf pan	Two 5¾-in. x 3-in. x 2-in. loaf pans
One 9-in. round baking pan	One 8-in. square baking dish
Two 9-in. round baking pans	One 13-in. x 9-in. x 2-in. baking pan
One 10-in. fluted tube pan	One 10-in. tube pan or two 9-in. x 5-in. x 3-in. loaf pans
One 13-in. x 9-in. x 2-in. baking pan	Two 9-in. round baking pans or two 8-in. square baking dishes

[12] *The Taste of Home Cookbook* (Reiman Media Group Inc., 2009).

HELPFUL HINTS [13]

- Baking powder and baking soda are leaveners that cause baked goods to rise and have a light texture.

- Baking powder can lose its ability to leaven. Discard any baking powder that is past the expiration date on the package.

- Baking soda is an alkaline substance used in batters that have acidic ingredients, such as buttermilk, molasses, and sour cream. When the baking soda is mixed with the acidic ingredient, there is an immediate release of carbon dioxide gas. Batter and dough that use only baking soda as a leavening agent should be baked right away; otherwise, the texture of the baked good will not be as light or rise as high.

- For testing the freshness of baking powder, mix 1 teaspoon baking powder and ⅓ cup hot water. For testing baking soda, mix ¼ teaspoon baking soda and 2 teaspoons vinegar. If bubbling occurs, the products are still fresh. If not, replace them.

- For quick breads, mix the dry and wet ingredients together until moistened. A few lumps in the batter are fine. Over mixing causes the gluten in the flour to develop and the texture to be coarse and tough.

- When baking quick breads place pans one inch apart and one inch from the sides of the oven for good air circulation. Rotate the pans halfway through the baking process. Leave in pan 10 minutes and remove to cooling rack. Most bread should cool completely before slicing so that it won't crumble.

- When baking breads, use aluminum baking pans and sheets that have a dull rather than shiny or dark finish for the best results. Grease only if requested in recipe. Fill pans ⅔ full for best results.

- For piecrust, measure all ingredients accurately. Mix flour and salt completely before adding shortening and water. Always use ice-cold water. Add an ice cube to water and measure before adding to flour. For a flaky crust, do not over mix; if over mixing occurs, the dough will become tough.

- To prevent sticking when rolling out piecrust, use a floured surface. Also, a pastry cloth and a rolling pin are a good investment; they keep the dough from sticking and decrease the amount of flour used.

- Always chill pastry dough for 30 minutes before rolling out to make it easier to handle.

- For best baking results, choose a dull-finished pan or a glass pie plate. These will produce golden, crisp crusts. Pans that are too shiny may produce crust that is soggy due to the high fat content in the dough. Do not grease the pie pan unless stated in the recipe.

- Preheat Oven 10 to 15 minutes before baking and place the pie in the center of the oven.

- Cakes are found in one of two categories: Butter cakes and Foam cakes. The batter of a butter cake consists of creaming fats such as butter or shortening with sugar. Butter cakes have a moist

118

[13] *The Taste of Home Cookbook* (Reiman Media Group Inc., 2009).

texture and a tender crumb. Foam cakes contain a high proportion of eggs and egg whites to flour. There are three types of foam cakes: angel food, sponge, and chiffon.

- When baking cakes, all-purpose flour is the most commonly used flour. Cake flour tends to give a more tender and delicate texture. Self-rising flour contains the leavening agent and salt, so you will only need to measure one ingredient. If you substitute one flour for another, you will need to make some adjustments:

  1. For 1 cup of cake flour, use ¾ cup plus 2 tablespoons all-purpose flour.

  2. For 1 cup all-purpose flour, use 1 cup plus 2 tablespoons cake flour.

  3. For 1 cup self-rising flour, place 1½ teaspoons baking powder and ½ teaspoons salt in a measuring cup. Add all-purpose flour to measure 1 cup.

- For best baking results, arrange oven racks so that the cake will bake in the center of the oven. Preheat oven for 10 to 15 minutes before baking.

- For better volume, allow the eggs to stand at room temperature for 30 minutes before using. Or place the eggs in a bowl of warm water while assembling the remaining ingredients.

- Mix dry ingredients together to evenly distribute the leavening agents throughout the flour.

- It is best to use the pan size called for in the recipe. For best results, use aluminum pans with a dull rather than shiny or dark finish. If using glass dishes, reduce the oven heat by 25°F.

- Grease and flour all butter cake recipes that will be removed from the pan. Fill the pans ¾ full. A thin batter will rise more than a thick one, so only fill the pans half full to allow room to rise.

- Leave one inch between pans and sides of oven. If baking more than one pan, stagger pans in the oven so that they are not directly over one another. Switch pan positions and rotate pans from front to back halfway through the baking time.

- Check for doneness at the minimum recommended baking time, then check every two minutes after that. Butter cakes are done when a toothpick inserted near the center of the cake comes out clean. Cool for ten minutes and loosen by running a knife around the edges. Turn out onto wire rack.

- If the cake sticks to the pan and will not come out, return to a warm oven for one minute and try again.

- To ice a cake with ease, wrap cake when cooled and place in the freezer for 2 to 3 hours, remove, place cake on a plate, and ice. Can remain in freezer for up to 2 months or until ready to ice and serve.

- Drop cookies: the consistency of a dropped cookie allows the dough to be dropped from a spoon onto the baking sheet, making it the easiest kind of cookie to make.

- Shaped cookies are shaped by hand into various shapes, such as balls, crescents, and logs, or they can be pressed down through a cookie press.

- Refrigerator cookies (icebox or slice-and-bake): the dough is shaped into logs, wrapped in plastic wrap, and refrigerated until firm enough to slice and bake.

- Cut-out cookies have firmer dough. The dough may be chilled before rolling out and cut into shapes with cookie cutters.

- Bar cookies consist of spreadable dough, a pourable batter, or a crumb crust that must be patted into the bottom of the pan. One thing that all bar cookies have in common is that they are baked in a pan rather than on a cookie sheet. After cooling, they are cut into bars.

- For best results, use butter, stick margarine, or shortening. Whipped tub, soft, liquid, or reduced-fat products contain air and water and will leave you with flat, tough, and under-browned cookies.

- For cookies, measure all ingredients accurately. Avoid over mixing the dough. If it is handled too much, the cookies will be tough.

- Always use heavy-gauge dull aluminum baking sheets. When a recipe calls for greased pans, use a cooking spray or shortening. Dark finishes will result in overly browned cookies.

- Preheat oven 10 to 15 minutes prior to baking. For even baking, make cookies the same size and thickness. Place cookie dough 2 to 3 inches apart. Leave at least 2 inches around the cookie sheet and the oven walls. For best results, bake only one sheet at a time. If you have to bake two at once, switch the position of the baking sheets halfway through the baking time.

- Unless otherwise stated, let the cookies cool for 1 minute before removing to cooling rack. Cool completely before storing.

- If wrapped correctly, cookies can stay in freezer up to 3 months. For best results, wrap separately and place in plastic container or plastic bag, seal, and place in freezer. Do not place icing on sugar cookies when freezing; it's best to ice them before serving.

- Cheesecakes: For best results, always use cream cheese and eggs at room temperature. Remove them from the refrigerator 1 hour before using. To soften cream cheese in the microwave, place an unwrapped (8 ounce) package of cream cheese on a microwavable plate; microwave on 50 percent power for about 30 to 60 seconds until soft. Make sure batter is completely free of lumps before adding eggs. Add eggs one at a time; beat on low after each addition. Open the oven door as little as possible, especially the first 30 minutes. Drafts can cause a cheesecake to crack.

RECIPES

Cream Cheese Icing

1 (8 ounce) package cream cheese, softened

½ cup butter, room temperature

2 teaspoons vanilla

16 to 24 ounces confectioners' sugar

Half and half

Whip cream cheese and butter together until light and fluffy. Add vanilla, then confectioners' sugar, one cup at a time, beating well after each. Add half and half to desired consistency. Mix until creamy and ice cake. <u>Note</u>: Double the recipe for a thick two-layered 9-inch cake.

German Chocolate Icing

1 cup sugar

1 cup evaporated milk

3 egg yolks, beaten

½ cup butter, cubed

1 teaspoon vanilla

1⅓ cups flaked coconut

1 cup pecans, chopped

1 square (1 ounce) semisweet chocolate

1 to 2 tablespoons oil

Heat sugar, milk, and egg yolks over medium heat until mixture thickens and is golden brown, stirring constantly. Remove from heat and add butter cubes; stir until melted. Add in vanilla, coconut, and nuts. Cool until thick enough to spread. Place icing between layers and on top of cake. Once icing is placed on the cake, melt chocolate in oil over low heat. Drizzle down the sides of the cake and chill. <u>Note</u>: Do not attempt to ice sides with coconut icing. Melted chocolate can be drizzled on sides or a chocolate butter cream icing can be placed on sides.

Old Fashioned Seven-Minute Icing

2 large egg whites, unbeaten

1½ cups sugar

2 teaspoons light corn syrup

Dash salt

¼ teaspoon cream of tartar

⅓ cup cold water

1 teaspoon vanilla

Place egg whites, sugar, corn syrup, salt, cream of tartar, and water in a double boiler, heat water to low boil over medium heat. As mixture warms, begin to beat with an electric mixer to blend. Beat constantly with mixer on high until frosting peaks appear, about seven minutes. Do not overcook. Remove pan from top of the boiling water. Add vanilla. Beat until spreading consistency. Frosts one 9x13 or a two-layer 8–9 inch cake. Great on coconut cake. <u>Note</u>: Good on top of Pound cake or Spice cake.

Chocolate Butter Cream Icing

3 sticks of butter, softened

2 tablespoons milk or half and half

1 (9 ounce) semisweet chocolate chips, melted

1 teaspoon vanilla

2¼ cups confectioners' sugar

Beat butter for 3 minutes. Add milk and beat until smooth. Add chocolate and beat additional 2 minutes. Add vanilla, beat 3 minutes longer, and then add in confectioners' sugar, until desired consistency.

Apple and Orange Glaze

2 large oranges

2 large apples

2 cups sugar

2 tablespoons water

Zest half of one orange to top cake, set aside. Zest remainder of orange peels; peel and grate apples. Place orange zest and grated apples, sugar, and 2 tablespoons of water in a cast iron skillet. Cook on low heat and stir regularly until color darkens and becomes golden brown. Let cool and spread over cake of choice. Top with orange zest.

Vanilla Frosting / Chocolate Frosting

⅓ cup butter, softened

3 cups confectioner's sugar

1½ teaspoons vanilla

1 to 2 tablespoons milk or half and half

Vanilla Frosting: Mix softened butter and confectioner's sugar with electric mixer on low speed. Add vanilla and milk a little at a time until desired thickness for spreading on cake is achieved. Frost a 9x13 cake or two, 8-inch or 9-inch layers.

Chocolate Frosting: Decrease confectioner's sugar to 2 cups and add 6 tablespoons of cocoa. Mix as directed above.

Old-Fashioned Sugar Cookies

1½ cups flour, sifted

½ teaspoon baking powder

½ teaspoon salt

½ teaspoon soda

¾ cup sugar

½ cup shortening

1 egg

2 heaping teaspoons milk

2 teaspoons vanilla

Preheat oven to 375°F. Sift together flour, baking powder, salt, soda, and sugar. Cut in shortening until mixture resembles coarse meal or small peas. Blend in egg, milk, and vanilla; roll out on floured board. Cut with cookie cutter; place on ungreased cookie sheets. Bake for 6 to 8 minutes.

Kelly's Very Favorite Sugar Cookie

5 cups all-purpose flour

2 cups sugar

1 teaspoon baking powder

¼ teaspoon baking soda

¼ teaspoon salt

1 cup butter (2 sticks), softened

4 large eggs, room temperature

¼ cup milk or half and half

2 teaspoons vanilla

Preheat oven to 350°F. In large bowl, mix together flour, sugar, baking powder, baking soda, and salt. Cut in butter until mixture resembles coarse crumbs. Add eggs and mix well. Beat in milk and vanilla. Cover and chill at least two hours. Work with one-third of the dough at a time on a well-floured surface; roll dough one-fourth to one-eighth-inch thick. Cut into shapes and place on lightly greased cookie sheet. Bake for 8 to 10 minutes, only until edges are the slightest brown. Cool 5 minutes; loosen cookies from cookie sheet. Ice cookies or dip in chocolate.

ICING:

2 cups sifted confectioners' sugar

2 tablespoons butter, softened

4 to 5 teaspoons milk

¼ teaspoon almond extract (optional)

In a small bowl, beat together confectioners' sugar, butter, and almond extract with electric mixer. Beat in milk until icing is of piping consistency. For spreadable icing, add more milk.

CHOCOLATE DIP:

1 (12 ounce) package semisweet or milk chocolate chips

4 to 6 tablespoons oil

On low heat, place oil and chocolate chips in saucepan, or use a double boiler. Stir continually as chocolate melts. When completely melted, remove from heat and dip one side of each heart cookie; place on parchment or wax paper atop cookie sheet. Chill to set. <u>Note</u>: Use Ghirardelli melting chocolates.

Mexican Wedding Cookies

1 cup butter, softened

1 cup confectioners' sugar, divided

1 teaspoon vanilla

¼ teaspoon salt

2 cups flour

1 cup nuts, chopped

Preheat oven to 375°F. In mixing bowl cream butter, ½ cup confectioner's sugar, vanilla, and salt until fluffy. Stir in flour until well blended. Add chopped nuts. Chill 30 minutes, until firm. Shape into a ball and place on cookie sheet. Bake 12 to 14 minutes until lightly golden. Remove from oven and drop into ½ cup confectioners' sugar to coat. Cool and store in airtight container.

Chocolate Fit for a Queen

CUPCAKE:

1½ cups all-purpose flour

½ teaspoon salt

1 teaspoon baking soda

1 cup sugar

¼ cup cocoa

1 cup water

⅓ cup oil

1 tablespoon vanilla

1 tablespoon Apple-cider vinegar

Preheat oven to 350°F. Mix dry ingredients. Add wet ingredients and mix until well blended. Scoop in paper-lined mini muffin pan two-thirds full.

FILLING:

1 (8 ounce) package cream cheese, softened

1 egg

½ cup sugar

½ teaspoon salt

1 teaspoon vanilla

1 (12 ounce) bag semisweet mini chocolate chips

Blend cream cheese and egg together in mixing bowl. Add sugar, salt, and vanilla until well blended. Fold in mini chocolate chips. Drop by teaspoon into center of batter. Bake 10 to 15 minutes, not to be overly browned.

Checkerboard Cake

2 cups all-purpose flour

½ cup Crisco or solid shortening

1½ cups sugar

1 cup milk, divided

1 teaspoon salt

3½ teaspoons baking powder

1 teaspoon vanilla

4 eggs, room temperature

Food coloring, 4 colors

Preheat oven to 350°F. Combine flour, Crisco, sugar, ⅔ cup milk, and salt in large bowl. Mix for 2 minutes with electric mixer. Add baking powder and mix again. Add ⅓ cup milk, vanilla, eggs; mix thoroughly. Separate batter into four bowls. Add a different color of food coloring to each bowl of batter. Grease and flour pans: two round cake pans or one 9x13 pan. Spoon a tablespoon of colored batter into pan, alternating colors as you cover bottom of pan. Because batter is thick, it will not spread. Begin another layer alternating colors until you use all of the batter. Bake for 20 to 25 minutes. Use toothpick to test for doneness. Frost with your favorite icing.

Pumpkin Cake Bars

4 eggs, room temperature

1 teaspoon cinnamon

1 (16 ounce) can pumpkin

½ teaspoon cloves

1 teaspoon ginger

1½ cups sugar

¼ teaspoon salt

1 box yellow cake mix

1 cup butter, melted

½ cup pecans, chopped

Preheat oven to 350°F. Mix the first seven ingredients together in a mixing bowl until well blended. Pour into a greased 9x13 pan and sprinkle the dry cake mix evenly over batter. Drizzle with melted butter and pecans, covering dry mix. Bake for 45 minutes. May need to cover the top with foil before time has expired to keep from browning too much. Chill and serve cold with whipped cream or ice cream.

Peanut Butter Swirl Brownies

BROWNIE:

1¼ cups all-purpose flour

¾ teaspoon baking powder

½ teaspoon salt

½ cup butter (1 stick)

4 (1 ounce) squares unsweetened chocolate

1½ cups sugar

2 teaspoons vanilla extract

4 large eggs, lightly beaten

PEANUT BUTTER SWIRL:

1 cup creamy peanut butter

⅓ cup sugar

4 (1 ounce) squares semisweet chocolate

1 teaspoon vanilla extract

1 large egg

Preheat oven to 350°F. Grease a 9x13 metal baking pan. Prepare Brownie: In mixing bowl, combine flour, baking powder, and salt. In 3-quart saucepan, heat butter and chocolates over low heat until melted, stirring frequently. Remove saucepan from heat; stir in sugar. Add vanilla and eggs; stir until well mixed. Stir flour mixture into chocolate mixture until blended. Pour batter into baking pan. Prepare

Peanut Butter Swirl: In medium bowl, with mixer at medium speed, beat peanut butter, sugar, flour, vanilla, and egg until well blended. Top the 2 cups of batter with six large dollops of peanut butter mixture. Spoon remaining chocolate batter over and between peanut butter in six large dollops. With tip of knife, cut and swirl in peanut butter. Bake brownie 30 to 35 minutes or until edge comes out almost clean. Cool in pan on wire rack.

Pumpkin Bars

4 eggs, room temperature

1⅔ cups granulated sugar

1 cup canola oil

1 (16 ounce) can pumpkin

2 cups all-purpose flour

2 teaspoons baking powder

2 teaspoons ground cinnamon

1 teaspoon salt

1 teaspoon baking soda

Preheat oven to 350°F. In mixing bowl, beat together eggs, sugar, oil, and pumpkin until light and fluffy. In a separate bowl, sift together flour, baking powder, cinnamon, salt, and soda. Add to pumpkin mixture and mix thoroughly. Spread batter in ungreased 15x10x1-inch pan. Bake for 25 to 30 minutes. Cool. Frost with cream cheese icing. Cut into bars.

ICING FOR PUMPKIN BARS:

1 (3 ounce) package cream cheese, softened

½ cup butter

1 teaspoon vanilla

2 cups powdered sugar

Blend cream cheese and butter together. Stir in vanilla. Add powdered sugar, a little at a time, beating well, until mixture is smooth. Spread on cake.

Cinnamon Chocolate Fudge Brownies

1 cup butter, softened

1 cup granulated sugar

1 cup brown sugar, firmly packed

4 large eggs, room temperature

1 cup unsweetened cocoa

2 teaspoons cinnamon

1 tablespoon vanilla

1 cup all-purpose flour

¾ cup milk chocolate chips

¾ cup pecans, chopped

Preheat oven to 350°F. Beat butter at medium speed until creamy; gradually add granulated and brown sugars, beating well. Add eggs, one at a time, just until blended. Add cocoa, cinnamon, and vanilla; beat until blended. Gradually add flour; beat well. Stir in chips and pecans. Pour batter into a greased 9x13 pan. Bake for 30 to 35 minutes. Cool and cut into squares.

Gooey St. Louis Brownies

BROWNIE:

¾ cup butter (1½ sticks)

6 (1 ounce) squares unsweetened chocolate

2 cups granulated sugar

1 teaspoon vanilla

3 large eggs, lightly beaten

1¼ cups all-purpose flour

½ teaspoon salt

GOOEY TOPPING:

2 large eggs

1 (8 ounce) package cream cheese, softened

2 cups confectioners' sugar

1 teaspoon vanilla

Preheat oven to 350°F. Grease 9x13 metal baking pan. Prepare Brownies: In 3-quart saucepan, heat butter and chocolate over medium-low heat until melted, stirring frequently. Remove saucepan from heat; stir in sugar and vanilla. Add eggs; stir until well mixed. Stir in flour and salt just until blended. Spread batter in pan. Prepare Gooey Topping: In medium bowl, with mixer at low speed, beat eggs, cream cheese, sugar, and vanilla until well combined. Gently spread topping over brownie. Bake brownie 55 to 60 minutes or until toothpick inserted 2 inches from edge comes out almost clean and top turns golden brown. Cool in pan on wire rack. When cool, cut brownie lengthwise into six strips, then cut each strip crosswise into six pieces.

Peanut Butter Cookies with a Kiss

1 (14 ounce) can sweetened condensed milk

1 cup chunky peanut butter

2 teaspoons vanilla extract

2 cups biscuit mix

Sugar for coating

Bag Hershey's Kisses

Preheat oven to at 350°F. Combine condensed milk and peanut butter in large bowl. Beat at medium speed until well blended. Add vanilla and biscuit mix; beat well. Shape dough into 1-inch balls; roll in sugar. Place 2 inches apart on ungreased cookie sheet. Dip fork in sugar and flatten cookie. Bake for 6 to 8 minutes. After removing from oven, immediately press one Hershey's Kiss into the center of each cookie. Remove to cooling rack.

Rocky Road Brownies

1¼ cups all-purpose flour

½ teaspoon baking powder

½ teaspoon salt

¾ cup butter (1½ sticks)

6 (1 ounce) squares unsweetened chocolate

2 cups sugar

2 teaspoons vanilla

5 large eggs, lightly beaten

2 cups miniature marshmallows

1½ cups assorted nuts, toasted and coarsely chopped

Preheat oven to 350°F. Grease 9x13 metal baking pan. In mixing bowl, combine flour, baking powder, and salt. In 3-quart saucepan, heat butter and chocolate over medium-low heat until melted, stirring frequently. Remove saucepan from heat; stir in sugar and vanilla. Add eggs; stir until well mixed. Stir flour mixture into chocolate mixture just until well blended. Spread batter in pan. Bake brownie 20 minutes or until toothpick inserted 2 inches from edge comes out almost clean. Sprinkle top of brownie evenly with marshmallows; top with nuts. Bake 5 minutes longer or until marshmallows melt slightly. Cool in pan on wire rack.

Raspberry Brownies

1 cup all-purpose flour

¾ cup unsweetened cocoa

½ teaspoon baking powder

½ teaspoon salt

1 cup butter (2 sticks)

1½ cups sugar

4 large eggs, room temperature

¾ cup seedless raspberry jam

2 teaspoons vanilla extract

¾ cup semisweet chocolate chips

Preheat oven to 350°F. Grease 9x13 metal baking pan. In bowl, combine, flour, cocoa, baking powder, and salt. In 3-quart saucepan, melt butter over medium-low heat. Remove saucepan from heat; with wire whisk, stir in sugar. Add eggs, one at a time, beating well after each addition. With spoon, stir flour mixture into chocolate mixture just until well blended. Whisk jam and vanilla until blended. Stir into brownie batter. Fold in chocolate chips. Spread batter in pan. Bake for 30 to 35 minutes or until toothpick inserted 2 inches from edge comes out almost clean. Cool in pan on wire rack. When cool, cut brownie lengthwise into six strips, then cut each strip crosswise into six pieces.

LEAH AND RACHEL
Women of Jealousy and Envy

Biblical Principle: A spirit of jealousy and envy robs us of the ability to accept and love others unconditionally.

Read Genesis Chapter 29—31.

1. How did Jacob come to meet Rachel?

2. What was he willing to sacrifice for her?

3. How did Laban trick (lie to) Jacob?

4. Which of Laban's daughters did Jacob end up with on his wedding night? Why?

5. We see deception throughout this family. What was required of Jacob in order to keep Rachel as his wife?

6. What is the game going on between these two sisters?

7. What was Rachel's solution to her barrenness? Did it work?

8. Does anyone win when there is rivalry and jealousy between women?

9. Name some of the tangible and nontangible things that are lost when jealousy, envy, and rivalry exist between women.

What I Learned Today

Week Seven

BREADS, COOKIES, & PIES

GIRL'S DAY OUT

hen you were a little girl, did you ever play house and pretend you were baking a cake? Did you ever have an Easy-Bake Oven? Oh, I did! Yes, on both accounts. However, I never found the Easy-Bake Oven to be easy, only messy. Did you ever notice how awful the Easy-Bake cake tasted? It was absolutely nothing like the cakes my mom used to make. I am glad I didn't base my baking ability on my failures with my Easy-Bake Oven!

Being a female, you know how much little girls like to play and pretend they are mommies, taking care of their baby dolls, cooking and baking cakes, just enjoying every part of their pretend play, without a care in the world.

I now have four granddaughters of varied ages. I have noticed something about them: not only do they love to pretend in their little play kitchen, they love to be in the kitchen with Mommy or Mimi. The oldest, Annalise, and I have a *Girls' Day Out* every three months. Each time I ask her what she wants to do, she answers, "Go to your house and bake." She loves to measure, pour, and break the eggs. One time, we bought an ironing board and iron, a play one, of course. We came back to the house and put on our aprons. She ironed her doll clothes while I got everything ready to bake. We had such a good time in the kitchen together. The cookies were so good hot out of the oven. Pop always enjoyed our *Girls' Day Out*. His favorite thing was a hot cookie right out of the oven; what man wouldn't? That day, Annalise and I were making a special memory. She loved being in the kitchen with Mimi. It might be the last time she will ever enjoy ironing, though!

---

peaking of special memories, when I was seven, I spent the summer with my grandparents. While there, I discovered a treasure under the basement stairwell. It was a wicker picnic basket, complete with plates, napkins, cups, forks, spoons, and a sweet little tablecloth. I spent hours playing with that basket and pretending to make all kinds of wonderful food for my pretend family. We would have cake, ice cream, cookies, and cupcakes. Nothing healthy, of course!

The fun part of pretend play is that you can bake anything your little heart desires and eat as much as you want. Oh, the hours of fun I had playing with that picnic basket!

Even now as a grown woman, I enjoy time in the kitchen baking special treats for my family, friends, and neighbors. It is a great way to bless those God has placed in our lives!

Let's Bake!

RECIPES

Chocolate Snowflake Cookies

2 cups sugar

½ cup vegetable oil

4 (1 ounce) squares unsweetened chocolate, melted

4 eggs, room temperature

2 teaspoons vanilla

2 cups all-purpose flour

2 teaspoons baking powder

½ teaspoon salt

¾ cup confectioners' sugar

Preheat oven to 350°F. Combine first three ingredients at medium speed. Slowly add eggs, vanilla, flour, baking powder, and salt. Dough will be sticky. Cover. Chill at least 2 hours. Shape dough into small balls. Roll in confectioners' sugar. Place cookies 2 inches apart on **greased** cookie sheet. Bake for 10 to 12 minutes. Remove immediately to cool on racks. <u>Note</u>: You must work quickly in shaping dough into balls.

PIES AND QUICHES

Nancy's Piecrust

⅓ cup ice cold water

⅓ cup Crisco shortening

1 cup all-purpose flour

Preheat oven to 375°F. Pour ⅓ cup cold water over a bowl of ice cubes—let stand for 5 minutes. In mixing bowl, cut shortening into flour with a fork or wire pastry blender. Sprinkle with ⅓ cup ice-cold water, 1 tablespoon at a time, tossing with fork or pastry blender until water is absorbed. Form into a ball and place onto lightly floured surface. Work dough together until smooth. With rolling pin, roll out from center to outside edge in all directions; watch for even thickness. Roll to extend 2 inches beyond pie pan; fold pastry into quarters. Place in pie pan and gently unfold. Press the edges using a fork, pressing along the edge or pinch edges. Tip: If baking without a filling, prick crust with fork and bake for 15 minutes. For baking crust with filling, follow recipe for the specific pie you are making. <u>Note</u>: Do not overwork dough, it will become tough.

Cathy's Easy Piecrust

7 tablespoons butter, melted

1 cup all-purpose flour

2 tablespoons milk

¼ teaspoon salt

Preheat oven to 425°F. Melt butter in saucepan over low heat. Remove from heat and add remaining ingredients. Stir until mixture forms a ball. Pat out dough onto floured surface. With rolling pin, roll out from center to outside edge in all directions; watch for even thickness. Roll to extend 2 inches beyond pie pan; fold pastry into quarters. Place in pie pan and gently unfold. Press the edges using a fork, pressing along the edge or pinch edges. If using a pudding filling, prick piecrust with fork tines and bake for 10-15 minutes. Cool. Fill baked pie crust with pudding and top with meringue or whipped cream. <u>Note</u>: For baking crust with filling, follow recipe for the specific pie you are making.

Short Cut to Great Piecrust

Are you short on time, short on patience, or just don't care if your pie is made with a homemade crust? Follow the steps below for a short cut to a great piecrust.

STEP #1: Get into your car and drive to the closest grocery store

STEP #2: Exit car and enter grocery store

STEP #3: Make your way to the dairy aisle

STEP #4: Locate the Pillsbury piecrust package, pick it up, and carry it to checkout

STEP #5: Pay the checker, pick up the bag with piecrust and return home

STEP #6: Preheat oven according to the package and follow directions

STEP #7: Bake according to the package and pie recipe

STEP #8: Tell your family how easy your pie was to make and then enjoy it!

Nancy's Meringue

For 9 inch pie:

3 egg whites, room temperature

1 teaspoon vanilla

¼ teaspoon cream of tartar

6 tablespoons sugar

For 8 inch pie:

2 egg whites, room temperature

½ teaspoon vanilla

¼ teaspoon cream of tartar

4 tablespoons sugar

Preheat oven to 350°F. Beat egg whites with vanilla and cream of tartar until smooth peaks form. Gradually add sugar, beating until stiff peaks form and sugar dissolves. Spread meringue over hot filling, sealing to edges of pastry. Bake for 12 to 15 minutes, or until meringue is golden. Cool. Before cutting meringue-topped pie, dip knife in water—no need to dry. This will cause knife to glide through the meringue and not stick.

Chocolate Chess Pie

1 cup sugar

6 tablespoons cocoa

¾ stick butter, melted

1½ teaspoons vanilla

3 eggs, beaten, room temperature

1 (4 ounce) can evaporated milk

Preheat oven to 350°F. Mix sugar and cocoa with melted butter and vanilla. Add beaten eggs, milk, and whisk thoroughly. Pour into unbaked pie shell. Bake for 30 to 35 minutes until set. It should have a slight movement in the middle of pie. Pie will continue to bake once removed from oven.

Cheri's Derby Pie

¼ cup butter, melted

1 cup sugar

1 teaspoon vanilla

2 eggs, beaten, room temperature

½ cup all-purpose flour

¾ cup nuts, chopped

1 cup semisweet chocolate chips

Preheat oven to 375°F. Mix butter, sugar, and vanilla until smooth and creamy. Blend in eggs one at a time. Add flour until blended well, and spoon in nuts and chocolate chips. Mix well and pour into pie shell. Bake for 30 minutes. Note: If gluten intolerant, make pie without crust in greased pie pan.

Walnut Fudge Pie

3 large eggs, room temperature

1 teaspoon vanilla

½ cup brown sugar, firmly packed

¼ cup all-purpose flour

¼ cup butter, melted

1 (12 ounce) package semisweet chocolate chips, melted

1½ cups walnuts, chopped

1 (15 ounce) package piecrust

Coffee ice cream

Preheat oven to 375°F. Stir together first five ingredients until blended. Mix in melted chocolate chips and nuts. Fit piecrust into pie plate. Fold edges under and crimp. Spoon filling into prepared pie crust. Bake for 30 minutes. Cool completely on wire rack. Serve with coffee ice cream.

Best Chess Pie

3 eggs, beaten, room temperature

1 cup sugar

1 teaspoon vanilla

6 tablespoons buttermilk

¾ stick butter, melted

1 (9 inch) unbaked pie shell

Preheat oven to 350°F. Mix the first five ingredients together, pour into pie shell. Bake at 350°F for 30 minutes, then for 10 minutes at 300°F or until set.

Mamaw's Coconut Pie

3 eggs, beaten, room temperature

1 cup sugar

¾ stick butter (6 tablespoons), melted

1 (9-inch) unbaked pie shell

6 tablespoons buttermilk

½ tablespoon vanilla

¾ cup coconut

Preheat oven to 350°F. Mix all together. Place in unbaked pie shell. Bake 35 to 45 minutes. Be sure pie is set before removing from oven.

Nancy's Creamy Chocolate Pie

1 cup sugar

⅓ cup all-purpose flour

2 cups milk or half and half

2 (1 ounce) squares of unsweetened chocolate

3 eggs, separated, room temperature

2 tablespoons butter

2 teaspoons vanilla

Preheat oven to 350°F. In saucepan, combine sugar, flour, and gradually stir in milk. Add in chocolate squares. Cook and stir over medium heat until bubbly. Cook and stir additional 2 minutes. Remove from heat. Pour small amount of hot mixture into yolks, mix thoroughly. Immediately pour egg yolk mixture into remaining hot mixture. Cook 2 minutes, stirring constantly. Remove from heat; add butter and vanilla. Pour into cooled, pre-baked pie shell. (See Nancy's Piecrust for directions.) Using egg whites, make meringue according to Nancy's Meringue recipe in lesson. Spread top of pie with meringue and bake for 12 to 15 minutes. Cool.

The Best Chocolate Pie

1½ cups sugar

2 tablespoons all-purpose flour

2 tablespoons cocoa, heaping

3 eggs, separated, room temperature

¾ cup half and half

2 tablespoons butter, melted

1 tablespoon vanilla

Preheat oven to 400°F. Mix together sugar, flour, and cocoa. In a separate bowl, mix egg yolks and milk. Pour milk mixture into dry mixture, mixing well. Add melted butter and vanilla; mix until well blended. Pour into an unbaked 9-inch pie shell. Bake at 400°F for 10 min. Reduce heat to 325°F and bake until set, usually about 35 to 40 minutes. Using egg whites, make meringue according to Nancy's Meringue recipe in lesson. Note: Do not store in refrigerator; meringue will separate from pie filling. If meringue is not desired, once the pie is cooled, it can be topped with fresh whipped cream. Recipe: 1 cup heavy whipping cream, 2 teaspoons vanilla, and 2 tablespoons confectioners' sugar. Place all ingredients in deep mixing bowl and whip on low for two minutes, then on high speed until light and fluffy. Top pie and serve.

Nancy's Coconut Cream Pie

¾ cup sugar

⅓ cup all-purpose flour

2 cups half and half

1 cup coconut plus 2 tablespoons

3 eggs, separated, room temperature

3 tablespoons butter

2 teaspoons vanilla

Preheat oven to 350°F. Crack and separate eggs, place yolks in one glass bowl, egg whites in another. In saucepan, combine sugar, flour, and gradually add milk. Cook and stir with whisk over medium heat until bubbly. Cook and stir an additional two minutes. Remove from heat. Pour small amount of hot mixture into egg yolks, mix thoroughly. Immediately pour egg yolk mixture into remaining hot mixture; Cook 2 minutes, stirring constantly. Remove from heat; add butter, vanilla, and coconut. Pour into pre-baked pie shell. Spread top with meringue, sprinkle with 2 tablespoons coconut, and bake for 12 to 15 minutes until lightly browned. Cool. Do not store in refrigerator; meringue will separate from pie filling. If meringue is not desire, once the pie is cooled, it can be topped with fresh whipped cream. Recipe: 1 cup heavy whipping cream, 2 teaspoons vanilla, and 2 tablespoons confectioners' sugar. Place all ingredients in deep mixing bowl and whip on low for two minutes, then on high speed until light and fluffy. Top pie and serve. When topped with whipped cream, the pie can be stored in refrigerator. Note: See Nancy's Piecrust recipe and Nancy's Meringue recipe in today's lesson.

Hot Apple Pie

Pastry for two-crust pie

¾ teaspoon nutmeg

⅓ to ⅔ cups sugar

Dash salt

2 (9-inch) unbaked pie shells

¼ cup all-purpose flour

1 teaspoon cinnamon

8 cups peeled tart apples, thinly sliced

3 tablespoons butter

Preheat oven to 425°F. Mix all dry ingredients in mixing bowl. Stir in apple slices. Turn into pastry lined pie plate. Place pats of butter on top evenly. Cover with top pastry, place slits in top, seal along edges, and flute. Cover edge with 3-inch foil pieces to prevent excess browning. Remove foil the last 15 minutes of baking. Bake 40 to 50 minutes or until crust is golden brown and juice begins to bubble through slits in top crust. Serve warm topped with ice cream.

Summer Quiche

1 deep-dish piecrust, baked partially and cooled

1 small red bell pepper, chopped

½ purple onion, chopped

2 garlic cloves, minced

2 tablespoons olive oil

2 tablespoons fresh basil, chopped

4 large eggs, beaten

1 cup half and half

1 teaspoon salt

½ teaspoon pepper

2 cups (8 ounces) Monterey Jack cheese, shredded

½ cup Parmesan cheese, shredded

3 plum tomatoes, cut into ¾-inch-thick slices

Preheat oven to 425°F. Fit piecrust into a 9-inch deep-dish tart pan or pie pan. Prick bottom and sides of piecrust with a fork. Bake for 10 minutes. Remove from the oven; set aside. Reduce oven temperature to 375°F. In a large skillet, sauté bell pepper, onion, and garlic in olive oil for 5 minutes, until tender; stir in basil. Whisk together eggs and the next three ingredients in a large bowl; stir in sautéed vegetables and cheeses. Pour into crust; top with sliced tomatoes. Bake quiche for 45 to 50 minutes, or until set, shielding edges with strips of foil after 30 minutes to prevent excessive browning. Let stand 5 minutes before serving. Note: Serve with a fresh salad.

Cathy's Easy Quiche

4 large eggs, beaten

⅓ cup mayonnaise

1 cup milk

Salt and pepper to taste

2 tablespoons flour

2 cups sharp Cheddar cheese, shredded, in plastic bag

Optional: 1 (9-inch) unbaked pie shell

Preheat oven to 375°F. In a mixing bowl, whisk together eggs, mayonnaise, milk, salt, and pepper. Add flour to the bag of cheese, close, and shake until cheese is coated with flour. Pour into egg mixture and stir. Pour into a greased 9-inch quiche pan or pie pan. Bake for 40 to 50 minutes or until center is set. Let stand 5 minutes before serving. Optional: Add cooked sausage, bacon, ham, chopped peppers, onions, broccoli, etc.

QUICK MIXES

Homemade Baking Powder

½ cup cream of tartar

½ cup arrowroot powder or cornstarch

¼ cup baking soda

Combine all ingredients in a small bowl and whisk gently until thoroughly mixed. Store in an airtight container and use in the same amounts as commercial baking powder. <u>Note</u>: Arrowroot can be found at natural foods stores. It is less processed than cornstarch.

Quick Baking Mix

8½ cups all-purpose flour

1 teaspoon baking soda

⅓ cup baking powder

2 teaspoons cream of tartar

1½ cups instant nonfat dry milk

1 tablespoon salt

2¼ cups vegetable shortening

Sift together all dry ingredients in a large mixing bowl. Use a wire whisk or large spoon to make sure everything is blended well. With a pastry blender, cut in shortening until evenly distributed. The mixture will resemble cornmeal in texture. Store in a large airtight container and put in a cool, dry place. Label the container with the contents and date. Use the mix within 10 to 12 weeks. <u>Note</u>: This baking mix can be used just as you would any commercial baking mix such as Bisquick® or Pioneer Mix.®

Biscuits

FAMILY SIZE:

3 cups Quick Baking Mix

⅔ cup milk or buttermilk

Yields: 18 (2-inch) biscuits

JUST FOR TWO:

1 cup Quick Baking Mix

3 tablespoons milk or buttermilk

Yields: 6 (2-inch) biscuits

Preheat oven to 450°F. Add milk to the Quick Baking Mix all at once, stirring twenty-five strokes. Knead dough fifteen strokes on floured cutting board or pastry cloth. Roll dough to ½-inch thick. Cut into rounds with biscuit cutter. An empty tin can that has been washed can also be used to cut biscuits. Place in a greased baking pan with sides of biscuits touching each other. Brush with melted butter. Bake for 10 to 12 minutes.

Pancakes

1 egg, beaten

1 teaspoon baking soda

3 cups Quick Baking Mix

1½ cups buttermilk

Beat the egg in a small bowl and stir in the buttermilk. Mix soda and liquid until blended. Bake on a hot griddle. Makes approximately 18 pancakes. Note: Any type of milk can be substituted for buttermilk.

Muffins

2½ cups Quick Baking Mix

4 tablespoons sugar

1 egg, beaten

1 cup milk

Preheat oven to 425°F. Grease or line a 12-cup muffin tin. In a medium bowl, combine Quick Baking mix and sugar and mix well. In a small bowl, combine beaten egg and milk. Add the liquid ingredients to the dry ingredients and stir until just blended. Fill muffin tins two-thirds full and bake for 15 to 20 minutes or until golden brown. Serve with butter and honey if desired. Variations: Add ½ cup chopped nuts or dried fruit to the dry ingredients before adding the liquid ingredients. Sprinkle cinnamon and sugar on the top of each muffin before baking. Add 1 cup fresh blueberries, washed and drained, to the dry ingredients before adding the liquid ingredients. Note: When adding the nuts or fruit, increase the baking time to 20 to 25 minutes.

Coffee Cake

3 cups Quick Baking Mix

⅓ cup sugar

1 egg, slightly beaten

1 cup milk

1 teaspoon vanilla

Cinnamon Crumble Topping

Preheat oven to 350°F. Grease an 8-inch or 9-inch square pan. Combine Quick Baking Mix and sugar in a medium bowl and whisk together. Combine beaten egg, milk, and vanilla in a small bowl and stir until blended. Add the liquid ingredients to the dry ingredients all at once. Fold the ingredients together until blended. Prepare the Cinnamon Crumble Topping:

⅓ cup all-purpose flour

½ cup brown sugar, firmly packed

1 teaspoon cinnamon

¼ cup butter

Combine the flour, sugar, and cinnamon in a medium bowl. Using a pastry blender or two knives cut the butter into the dry ingredients until the mixture is crumbly. Spread one-half of the cake batter into the greased pan. Top with one half of the topping mix. Repeat and end with the remaining topping mix. Bake 40 to 50 minutes.

QUICK BREAD RECIPES

Poppy Seed Bread

3 cups all-purpose flour

½ teaspoon salt

2¼ cups sugar

1½ teaspoons baking powder

3 eggs, room temperature

1⅛ cups Canola oil

1½ cups milk

2 teaspoons poppy seeds

1½ teaspoons almond extract

1½ teaspoons butter extract

1½ teaspoons vanilla extract

Preheat oven to 350°F. Mix flour, salt, sugar, and baking powder in a bowl. In another bowl, mix the rest of the ingredients. Combine both bowls of ingredients and mix well. Pour into greased loaf pans. <u>Note</u>: For a large loaf, bake for 1 hour. For mini loaves, bake for 45 minutes or until brown and toothpick inserted comes out clean. Mix the following ingredients and pour glaze over warm Poppy Seed bread:

½ cup orange juice

1 cup powdered sugar

1½ teaspoons almond extract

1½ teaspoons butter extract

Strawberry Bread

3 cups all-purpose flour

2 tablespoons cinnamon

1 tablespoon allspice

1 teaspoon soda

1 teaspoon salt

2 cups sugar

4 eggs, room temperature

1¼ cups oil

2 small containers frozen strawberries, thawed and pureed in blender

Preheat oven to 350°F. Combine dry ingredients. Add eggs and oil, mix well. Blend wet and dry ingredients together. Fold strawberries into batter. Pour batter into two greased loaf pans and bake 45 to 50 minutes, until tops spring back when touched. <u>Note</u>: For mini loaves, bake for 45 minutes or until brown and toothpick inserted comes out clean.

Zucchini Bread

3 eggs, slightly beaten

1 cup Canola oil

2 cups sugar

½ cup brown sugar, firmly packed

3 teaspoons vanilla

2 cups peeled zucchini, grated

3 cups all-purpose flour

1 teaspoon salt

1 teaspoon baking soda

2 teaspoons cinnamon

1 teaspoon allspice

1½ teaspoon baking powder

1 cup nuts, chopped

½ cup raisins, optional

¼ cup carrots, shredded, optional

Preheat oven to 350°F. Mix eggs, Canola oil, sugars, and vanilla. Sift together flour, salt, baking soda, cinnamon, allspice, and baking powder. Combine wet and dry ingredients together. Fold zucchini and carrots into mixture Pour into two greased loaf pans and bake for 55 to 60 minutes or until top springs back and toothpick inserted in top comes out clean. <u>Note</u>: If desired add: 1 cup nuts, chopped or ½ cup raisins. For mini loaves, bake for 40 to 45 minutes or until brown and toothpick inserted comes out clean.

Applesauce Nut Bread

BREAD:

¾ cup sugar

⅓ cup canola oil

2 eggs, room temperature

3 tablespoons milk

1 teaspoon baking soda

½ teaspoon ground cinnamon

¼ teaspoon ground nutmeg

1 cup applesauce, chunky

2 cups all-purpose flour, sifted

½ teaspoon baking powder

¾ cup pecans, chopped

½ cup raisins

TOPPING:

¼ cup brown sugar, firmly packed

¼ cup pecans, chopped

½ teaspoon ground cinnamon

2 tablespoons confectioners' sugar (reserve for dusting)

Preheat oven to 350°F. Mix topping ingredients together, set aside. Combine all bread ingredients, mixing well. Turn the batter into a well-greased 9x5-inch loaf pan. Sprinkle topping evenly over top of batter. Bake for 1 hour. Cap loosely with foil the first 30 minutes of baking to prevent browning. Cool on rack. Dust with confectioners' sugar.

YEAST BREAD RECIPES

Easy Yeast Rolls

1 cup boiling water

¼ cup shortening

4 tablespoons butter

⅓ cup sugar

1 envelope rapid-rise dry yeast

1 egg, room temperature

1 teaspoon salt

2 to 3 cups all-purpose flour

Butter, melted

Preheat oven to 350°F. In medium bowl, pour boiling water over shortening and butter. Stir until melted. Blend in sugar and mix until cool. Add yeast and stir until dissolved. Add egg and salt. Sift flour into mixture one cup at a time, adding enough flour to make soft dough. Cover and refrigerate overnight. The next day, shape rolls by hand and place on a greased cookie sheet. Let rise for 1 to 2 hours or until doubled in size. Bake for 10 to 15 minutes, until golden brown. Brush tops with melted butter before or immediately after baking. <u>Note</u>: Whole-wheat flour can be substituted for all-purpose flour.

Buttery Herb Dinner Biscuits

½ cup butter

1 cup White Cheddar cheese, grated

2 cups self-rising flour

½ teaspoon thyme

½ teaspoon rosemary

¼ teaspoon parsley

1 cup sour cream

¼ cup Parmesan cheese, grated

Preheat oven to 350°F. In saucepan over med-low heat, melt butter and add Cheddar cheese until melted. In mixing bowl, place flour; blend in thyme, rosemary, and parsley. Pour melted butter, sour cream, and cheese over flour mixture and blend well. Let stand 10 minutes. Grease mini muffin pan and fill each cup two-thirds full. Sprinkle tops with Parmesan cheese. Bake for 15 to 20 minutes, until done.

Mom's Christmas Pastry

DOUGH:

⅓ cup warm water

1 tablespoon sugar

2 packages dry yeast

1 cup boiling water

1 stick butter

1½ teaspoons salt

1 large egg

4 cups all-purpose flour

Preheat oven to 350°F. Mix first 3 ingredients thoroughly and set aside to rise. Melt 1 stick of butter in 1 cup boiling water. Cool. While yeast is rising and water cooling, make nut filling.

NUT FILLING:

8 egg whites, room temperature

1 cup sugar

½ teaspoon salt

2 teaspoons almond extract

1 cup almonds, ground

1 cup pecans, ground

Filling: Beat egg whites and sugar at medium speed until blended, and then on high speed until stiff peaks form. Fold in salt, almond extract, and ground nuts and mix well. Chill.

In large mixing bowl, once boiling water with butter has cooled, add in yeast mixture. Mix in 1½ teaspoons salt and 1 large egg. Blend in 4 cups all-purpose flour. Once thoroughly blended, turn into greased bowl and let rise in warm place until doubled. Once doubled, roll out and knead dough; divide into six balls. Roll one at a time out onto floured surface until 8 to 10 inches in diameter and spread filling evenly onto pastry dough, stopping a half inch from edge of pastry. Tightly roll each, sealing ends and edges by pinching dough together. Turn ends under pastry roll to seal and secure leakages. Place on greased cookie sheet, seam side down. Brush top with a light coating of milk. Bake 10 to 15 minutes until lightly brown. While warm, top with glaze.

Glaze: Combine 3 tablespoons butter, melted, 1 cup confectioners' sugar, 4 to 6 teaspoons milk, and 2 teaspoons almond extract. Mix thoroughly. Amount of sugar may vary to attain the right consistency for glaze. Pour over warm pas- tries. Cool completely and serve or wrap in plastic wrap and freeze for later use. <u>Note</u>: Great breakfast or brunch pastry any time of the year.

Cinnamon English Muffin Bread

Cornmeal

½ cup water

2 cups milk

5 cups all-purpose flour, divided

2 (¼-ounce) envelopes active dry yeast

¼ teaspoon baking soda

2 teaspoons salt

1 tablespoon sugar

2 teaspoons ground cinnamon

1 cup raisins, optional

Preheat oven to 400°F. Grease two 9x5-inch loaf pans and coat with cornmeal. Set loaf pans aside. Combine water and milk in a saucepan; heat over medium heat just until hot. In large mixing bowl, combine 3 cups flour, yeast, baking soda, salt, sugar and cinnamon. Gradually add liquid to dry ingredients beating at high speed with an electric mixer. Beat an additional 2 minutes at medium speed. Stir in raisins. Gradually stir in remaining 2 cups of flour making a soft dough. Spoon dough into prepared loaf pans. Sprinkle top with cornmeal. Cover and let rise in a warm place until doubled; approximately 45 minutes. Bake for 25 minutes. Remove bread from pans immediately; cool of wire rack.

Oatmeal Wheat Bread

2½ cups buttermilk

¼ cup molasses

¼ cup honey

⅓ cup butter

2 packages yeast

1 ½ cups oatmeal

1 tablespoon salt

2 eggs

3 cups wheat flour

Preheat oven to 350°F. In saucepan over medium-low heat, mix buttermilk, molasses, honey, and butter. Cook until butter is melted and ingredients are blended. In large bowl, mix yeast, oatmeal, and salt. Beat eggs and add to cooled buttermilk mixture. Pour cooled liquid into oatmeal mixture and stir. Using a spoon, stir in 2½-3 cups wheat flour until incorporated. Dough will be stiff. Melt 3 tablespoons butter and brush top. Cover bowl and let rise until double. Punch down, shape into loaves. Place in greased loaf pans and bake for 30-35 minutes.

MIRIAM
A Woman with a Critical Spirit

Biblical Principle: A heart filled with jealousy can lead to a spirit of criticism.

Read Exodus Chapters 1—7, 11—15, 24, and Numbers Chapters 11—12.

1. Who was Miriam?

2. How did young Miriam watch over her brother?

3. As a grown woman, how do the scriptures describe Miriam?

4. Miriam's heart attitude started with *jealousy*, then moved to *complaining*, and ended with a *critical spirit*. We can see the progression of sin. Jealousy was the seed that took root and grew into a spirit of complaining, and then into a full-grown spirit of criticism. Prayerfully consider if you have a spirit of jealousy that has taken root and is growing into a spirit of complaining and criticism. When we ask God to show us if this our heart, He will! Write down your prayer of confession and turn from this sin.

5. God called all three to meet him—Miriam, Aaron, and Moses. Why is this?

6. God is serious about unconfessed sin in our lives. What was the punishment for Miriam's sin? How do we see the mercy of God on her behalf?

7. What lessons have you learned from Miriam that you will be applying to your own life?

What I Learned Today

Week Eight

HOSPITALITY

AN EXAMPLE TO FOLLOW

I mentioned previously that I grew up in a modest home. We had very few of what you might call expensive or elegant possessions, especially in the area of entertaining. Yet, our home was always open to anyone and everyone. It didn't matter the color of your skin, your background, or your economic status, you were always welcome! My dad was a college professor. Over the years, my mom taught young people from middle school up to the college level. So students were always welcome in our home. Mom and Dad were both very personable, and folks were always drawn to them. Their hearts were bigger than they were!

My parents eloped and married when Dad was twenty and Mom was seventeen. They didn't have a wedding registry. There were no pre-wedding showers and no beautiful wedding gifts, as we often see today. I do believe they had one wedding shower, once they arrived home. You did not find twelve-piece place settings of Wedgewood China or the latest pottery pattern in our home. There was no • Arte Italica and certainly no sterling silver flatware. Yet, none of this mattered. I don't think anyone who came to our home left there saying, "Can you believe she did not even have a twelve-piece place setting of her everyday dishes?" Instead, they went away feeling loved, cared for, having laughed a lot, and with memories of a good time in our home.

Why is it that in our "keeping up with the Joneses" society we let the things we do not have keep us from using what we do have to minister and bless others? The prevailing attitude today is that we have to possess certain things before we can invite others into our home. Where did this attitude come from? When that is your attitude, you miss out on relationships that could have blessed, challenged, and enriched your life.

I have heard young women say, "I don't set a beautiful table like Libby," or "I can't cook like Casey." Who cares! Who says you're supposed to be like Libby or Casey anyway? If my parents had had that attitude or those thoughts, I would have missed out on so much. I wouldn't have the fond memories of fun times with so many special people. I still remember sitting on the floor in our living room while the guest preacher sat in the only chair. It was nestled in the corner of the room near the opening to the kitchen. He told us story after story, and the three of us kids just laughed and laughed as he entertained us. What if my parents had said, "Our house is too small and too sparsely furnished to have the guest preacher stay with us?" What if my mom had said she couldn't have the guest preacher because she couldn't cook like Mrs. Smith?

I am grateful my parents were willing to open our home and be hospitable to anyone and everyone who entered there. How interesting that my siblings and I love to invite people into our homes. All four of us desire to be hospitable to others. We now have the joy of seeing our children desiring to do the same. My parents set the example for me; now my girls are setting an example for their children. Oh, what fond memories my grandchildren will have!

HELPFUL HINTS [14]

APPETIZERS: The purpose of serving appetizers is to promote conversation among your guests and to stimulate their appetite before serving the meal.

HOW MUCH TO SERVE: The amount per person will vary on the length of the party and the focus of the appetizers. For a social hour before dinner, plan on serving three to four different appetizers and allow four to five bites per person. For an open-house affair, plan on serving four to five different appetizers and allow four to six bites per person per hour. For an appetizer buffet that is served in place of a meal, plan on serving six to eight different appetizers and allow ten to fourteen bites per person.

TIPS FOR SERVING TASTY APPETIZERS [15]

1. Always allow cheese balls, dips, and spreads that contain cream cheese to stand at room temperature for 15 minutes before serving for easier spreading and better flavor.

2. Place dips in colorful, edible bowls, such as red or green cabbage shells or cored sweet yellow, red, orange, or green peppers.

3. For vegetables, tenderize firm vegetables, such as broccoli, green beans, and cauliflower by blanching them in boiling water for a minute or two to cook partially. They are to remain crisp. After you have blanched, immediately plunge the vegetables in ice water to stop the cooking. Drain before serving.

4. To garnish platters of appetizers, use sprigs of freshly picked herbs, lemon wedges, grape clusters, fresh berries, or small hot peppers. For a lighter feel, decorate with citrus peel curls, fresh chives, or edible flowers.

5. For additional vegetable options for dipping, use radishes, sweet red pepper strips, sugar snap peas, and cherry tomatoes.

6. Prepare appetizers ahead of serving time but store in the refrigerator; wrap tightly with foil or plastic wrap.

7. Keep cold appetizers on ice when your gathering takes you out-of-doors in the warm months, and keep hot appetizers hot to keep them safe from spoilage.

8. You can choose from hot, cold, and room temperature foods. When you select your appetizers, choose recipes that will give a variety of colors, textures (soft or crunchy), and flavors (sour, salty, savory, sweet, spicy, and subtle). Look for recipes that would make a nice presentation and require no last-minute fussing.

[14] *The Taste of Home Cookbook* (Reiman Media Group, 2009).
[15] *A Collection of Favorite Recipes by Cherry House Furniture Galleries* (Cookbooks by Morris Press, 2001).

ICEBREAKERS

1. Communication: Divide into two teams and give each team member a card with a number on it. Example: If there are six members on a team, cards would be numbered from 1 to 6. They have to arrange themselves in numerical order without talking or holding up fingers. They make up their own sublanguage or sign language and it is often pretty amusing. <u>Note</u>: Use the alphabet instead of numbers. Teams have to arrange themselves in alphabetical order without talking or using their hands.

2. Paper Roll: Get a roll of toilet paper and pass it around, instructing those playing to take as many sheets as they think they will need. Do not tell them what they will be doing with it. Once everyone has their sheets of paper, instruct them to tell the group one thing about themselves for every sheet of paper they are holding in their hand.

3. M&M Game: Pass around a bowl of M&Ms and tell everyone to take as many as they would like. For each color have a question for them to answer. For instance, red could be, "What was your most embarrassing moment?" You can play until all the M&Ms in each of their hands is gone. The best part of this game is you get to eat the M&Ms after you answer.

BEVERAGES

1. Make your own spiced tea or cider. Place orange peels, whole cloves, and cinnamon sticks in a 6-inch square piece of cheesecloth. Gather the corners and tie with string. Steep in hot cider or tea for 10 minutes or longer if you want a stronger flavor.

2. Always chill juices or sodas before adding to beverage recipes.

3. To cool your punch, float an ice ring made from the punch rather than using ice cubes. Not only is this more decorative, but it also inhibits melting and diluting. Place fresh or dried mint in the bottom of a cup of hot cocoa for a cool and refreshing taste.

4. One lemon yields about ¼ cup juice; one orange yields about ⅓ cup juice. This is helpful in making fresh lemonade or orange juice.

5. Never boil coffee; it brings out the acid and causes a bitter taste. Store ground coffee in the refrigerator or freezer to keep fresh.

6. Always use cold water for electric drip coffeemakers. Use 1 to 2 tablespoons ground coffee for each cup of water.

7. For easy fresh tea, place four to five family-size tea bags in the drip coffeemaker; pour 4 cups of water in, heat, and let water run through coffeemaker. Pour into a 64 ounce pitcher, add 2 to 3 cups of sugar, and stir. Fill remaining pitcher with cold water. Place in refrigerator until chilled.

EASY CENTER PIECES

1. For a special tea or luncheon, take small, clear, glass votive holders and wrap them with squares of decorative rice or glassine paper and tie with a contrasting ribbon or raffia.

2. For a fall idea, take miniature pumpkins, hollow them out, and place a votive or tea light inside. If you use votives, tie a fall ribbon around the top of the votives.

3. Use a variety of glass vases and go out into your yard cutting clippings of whatever you can find. If you need more color, buy a large daisy for the center of each vase.

4. For a bouquet of fresh flowers, arrange in a vase using an Easy Arranger—a wire catcher that sits on top of most vases and provides a wonderful spaced pattern into which you can slip flower stems to make a beautiful bouquet.

5. Take a medium, round, low-sitting vase, place ½ cup water in base, and lay a hydrangea with stem removed into the water. Take three tulips cutting stems in order that the tulips will just fit down into the vase with stems pushing down into the hydrangea reaching the water. Stems of tulip should be slightly curved.

RULES OF ETIQUETTE

1. When meal planning, use recipes that contain a variety of foods, flavors, colors, and textures. Always begin your menu planning with the main dish, next side dishes and desserts; all are to complement the main dish.

2. Select recipes that can be prepared and served together in an allotted time frame, such as dishes that can be baked at the same temperature without any adjustments.

3. Once the meal planning is complete, make a shopping list according to the layout of your grocery store to reduce shopping time.

4. Be sure to serve hot foods hot and cold foods cold. Do not let any food remain at room temperature for more than two hours (one hour in hot weather).

5. Elbows off the table!

6. Power off! There is nothing more courteous than giving your full attention to the person you're with, which means no cell phones at the table, not even on vibrate! No matter how important the call, your dinner companions are more important!

7. Get a grip on things! If you find yourself confused about the proper usage of the utensils at a table setting, begin by using the utensils on the outside and work your way in. Do not hold your utensils like a shovel; use them as a guide.

8. Men need to understand that chivalry really matters. At formal dinners, they are to pull out the chair of the woman to their right.

9. If you leave the table during the meal, place the napkin to the left of your plate until you return. Remember, when you are finished eating, place the handles of your utensils at four o'clock on the round plate, pointed toward ten o'clock.

10. Serving dishes should be passed counterclockwise around the table.

HOSPITALITY MADE FUN
AND AFFORDABLE

*Below are fun, easy, and inexpensive ways
to host family and friends...*

HOT DOG BAR

Grilling hotdogs for your friends is great for those friends who have children. Once hotdogs are cooked, have a condiment bar with a variety of toppings. Choices could be: melted Cheddar cheese, relish, a variety of mustards, ketchup, chopped onion, chopped peppers (green, red, yellow, jalapeño), and chili. You could have Mexican dogs or veggie dogs; be creative.

$1 PIZZAS MADE EDIBLE

Purchase small individual dollar pizzas and set up a topping bar. Choices could be a variety of fresh chopped vegetables, a variety of peppers, avocado, spinach, fresh corn cut from the cob, tomatoes, etc. Have a variety of cheeses available as well as other toppings, such as salsa, Alfredo sauce, etc. Different meats to have on hand: sausage, pepperoni, ground beef, Canadian bacon, etc. Each guest could be asked to bring a topping. The children will have fun creating their own pizza.

MEXICAN TRAIN WRECK

Each guest is asked to bring one of the following ingredients:

Tortilla chips/flour tortillas	Guacamole
Chopped tomatoes,	Shredded lettuce
Chopped onions/peppers	Chopped cilantro
Salsa	Hot cheese dip etc.
Grated cheeses/cheese sauce	Meat item, hostess choice

Allow everyone to go thru the buffet line creating their own Mexican train wreck. Hostess will provide the meat item. Enjoy sopaipillas for dessert.

POTATO BAR

The weather is getting cooler and fall is in the air. Your husband has decided at the last minute to invite some friends over to watch the opening game of the college football season. What are you going to serve when you only have two hours? How about a potato bar? Crank up the oven and in an hour and a half you will have hot potatoes with lots of toppings to serve. Be creative and pull out some unusual items to top those potatoes. Example: leftover grilled chicken breast, roasted chicken, browned hamburger, cooked bacon, a variety of cheeses, salsa, chopped onion, chopped sweet peppers, sour cream, plain yogurt, guacamole, chopped tomatoes, spinach, or leftover roasted vegetables. Be creative; after all, you were not expecting company, so see what you have on hand.

SOUP AND SALAD NIGHT

In the winter, everyone loves a bowl of hot soup and a good fresh salad. Try this easy soup and salad recipe.

Sausage Vegetable Stew

1 medium purple onion, diced

4 cloves garlic, smashed

3 tablespoons olive oil

2 tablespoons butter

1 tablespoon Spanish paprika

1 teaspoon Kosher salt

3 tablespoons flour

3 cups water

4 medium carrots, peeled, cut into small chunks

14 ounces small, red potatoes, quartered

1 (12 ounce) package Kielbasa sausage, cut into slices

1 tablespoon Apple Cider vinegar

Salt and pepper to taste

2 tablespoons cornstarch

1 tablespoon warm water

2 tablespoons sour cream

1 tablespoon fresh parsley, chopped

Dash of paprika

Cook onion and garlic in oil and butter. Add Spanish paprika, kosher salt, and flour. Whisk in water. Add carrots and red potatoes. Bring to a boil; reduce heat to medium. Cook until vegetables are tender. Add Kielbasa sausage. Add cider vinegar, salt, and pepper to taste. Cook additional 15 minutes. For thickening, in a small bowl, mix the cornstarch with warm water. Mixture should be a thin to medium consistency. Stir into soup. Cook until thickened and bubbly. Serve in a bowl topped with sour cream, fresh parsley, and a dash of paprika. For serving more than four, double the recipe. Note: All-purpose flour can be substituted for cornstarch.

Bibb Salad with Raspberry Dressing

2 tablespoons Raspberry vinegar

1 tablespoon Maple syrup

⅓ cup oil

1 head Bib lettuce, torn

Small purple onion, sliced

1 (2 ounce) Blue cheese, crumbled (cheese of choice)

2 tablespoons Pine nuts, toasted

Combine vinegar, syrup, and oil. Whisk and chill. Arrange torn lettuce; top with rings of purple onion. Top with blue cheese crumbles and toasted nuts. Drizzle with dressing.

IT'S DESSERT ONLY

Tired of spending so much time preparing meals for company? Just invite your friends over for a "dessert only" gathering. Have a cake, brownies, cookies, or ice cream. Build your own sundae bar or whatever you would like. The children would love to make their own slice-and-bake cookies and then ice them. Keep it simple and use paper bowls and plastic silverware; that way you will have more time to visit.

WE'VE GOT SOUL

Guests are to bring their favorite *soul* food, such as fried chicken, black-eyed peas, mashed potatoes, okra, pork ribs, corn bread, and fried green tomatoes. Be creative! A potluck every momma will love!

YOU BRING THIS, AND I'LL BRING THAT

Do not bear the total expense for having a large group of guests in for dinner. Assign each guest a dish to bring. Everyone gets to participate, and you won't stress out your husband with a huge grocery bill. Ask guests to bring their recipes to share, which will be a bonus for everyone!

LEFTOVER BUFFET

Maybe if you do not like your leftovers, your friends will! Why let it all go to waste? This idea will make for a very interesting meal. Lay out all the leftovers your friends have brought along with yours and dig in!

CHILI COOK-OFF

This is a great winter sports dinner idea, and the guys really get into seeing which one can make the best award-winning chili. Are you craving a bowl of chili? Call your friends and challenge them to a contest.

ICE CREAM BAR

Have everyone bring different types of ice cream and toppings. Don't forget the whipping cream! Have fun building your ice cream bar.

IT'S A SMALL WORLD AFTER ALL

Have an international potluck with specialty dishes from all around the world. Your table will be filled with vibrant colors and an inviting atmosphere. Have guests bring a dish of Italian, Mexican, French, German, African, Greek, Chinese, Japanese, or Thai cuisine—their choice! The possibilities are absolutely endless! For fun, have each guest dress according to the country their food represents.

ABC'S

Assign each couple a letter of the alphabet, asking them to bring a food beginning with that letter. Makes for an eclectic meal!

CAN WE SAY COMFORT!

Have guests bring their homestyle favorites, such as macaroni and cheese, mashed potatoes and gravy, meatloaf, chicken and dumplings, apple pie, or chocolate chip cookies and ice cream. Mmm, good! Oh what comfort!

APPETIZER RECIPES

Sausage Pizza Bites

1 pound breakfast sausage

1 pound lean ground beef

2 tablespoons parsley

1 teaspoon oregano

½ teaspoon basil

½ teaspoon garlic salt

1 pound Velveeta cheese or 2 (8 ounce) cream cheese

Party Rye bread

Brown meats; drain well. Return to skillet and add spices and cheese. Stir until cheese is melted. Spread on party rye bread or onto full-size slices, cut in fourths. Place under broiler for a few minutes until hot and lightly browned. <u>Note</u>: Bites may be frozen on cookie sheets before broiling. Once frozen, place in plastic bags. When ready to serve, remove from freezer and place on cookie sheets and broil.

Chutney Cheese Spread

3 cups sharp Cheddar cheese, grated

1 cup mayonnaise

1 small package almonds, slivered

Dash of Tabasco

1 bunch green onions, chopped

Major Grey's chutney (found in mayo, mustard section of grocery)

4 slices bacon, cooked crisp and crumbled

Combine Cheddar cheese, mayo, almonds, Tabasco, and green onions. Place in a parchment-lined container. <u>Note</u>: Plastic wrap will work as well. Refrigerate overnight until set. Turn out onto serving piece and cover with chutney and bacon bits. Serve with Ritz crackers.

Nancy's Dip

2 (8 ounce) packages Monterey Jack cheese, shredded

1 small can of green chilies, drained and chopped

1 (3 ounce) can sliced black olives, drained

1 (8 ounce) bottle Wish Bone Italian Dressing

2 tomatoes, chopped

Mix together the above ingredients and refrigerate. Serve with any type corn chips.

Better than Dip

½ cup mayonnaise

1 (8 ounce) package cream cheese, softened

1 (8 ounce) package Swiss cheese, shredded

6 slices bacon, crisp and crumbled

¼ onion, chopped

1 sleeve Ritz crackers, crushed

Preheat oven to 350°F. Mix mayo, cream cheese, Swiss cheese, bacon pieces, and onion. Spray a square Pyrex dish with non-stick spray and evenly spread mixture into pan. Cover with crushed Ritz crackers. Bake for 20 to 25 minutes until bubbly. Great with Fritos.

Hot Chipped Beef Dip

3 (6 ounce) glass jars chipped beef, chopped

4 tablespoons butter

2 (8 ounce) packages cream cheese, softened

4 tablespoons milk

1 cup sour cream

½ cup green pepper, finely chopped

2 tablespoons onion, finely diced

½ teaspoon pepper

1 tablespoon garlic powder

1 cup whole pecans, chopped

Preheat oven to 350°F. Briefly sauté beef in butter. In mixing bowl, add to cream cheese, mix with electric mixer until well blended. Add remaining ingredients and mix well. Place in baking dish. Top with chopped pecans. Bake for 20 minutes. Serve with crackers.

Pat's Pimento Cheese

8 to 12 ounces extra sharp Cheddar cheese, grated

1 (4 ounce) jar pimentos, chopped

⅓ cup mayonnaise

¼ cup milk

1 tablespoon Worcestershire sauce

½ teaspoon garlic salt

Place all ingredients in food processor, blend until smooth. Note: This recipe works well as an appetizer on crackers, rye bread, or for a luncheon sandwich. Once refrigerated, keeps for up to two weeks.

Nutty Cheese Spread

1 (8 ounce) package cream cheese, softened

⅓ cup mayonnaise

1½ cups Swiss cheese, shredded

2 green onions, chopped

⅓ cup sliced almonds or walnut pieces

½ teaspoon ground nutmeg

⅛ teaspoon red pepper

Garnish, toasted almonds or walnuts

Preheat oven to 350°F. Combine first seven ingredients, mixing well. Spread cheese mixture into a square, glass baking dish. Bake uncovered for 15 to 20 minutes. Garnish and serve with crackers.

Colorado Caviar

Combine the following ingredients in a large bowl and stir carefully:

2 cans black beans, drain and rinse

1 can whole kernel yellow corn, drain and rinse

1 avocado, cut up

1 small red onion, chopped

2 (or more) Roma tomatoes, chopped

¼ cup cilantro, chopped

Mix the following and pour over the above mixture:

4 tablespoons lime juice

2 tablespoons olive oil

1 tablespoon Red wine vinegar

1 teaspoon salt

¼ teaspoon pepper

Chill and serve with Scoops or other chips. <u>Note</u>: Remains fresh for 2 to 4 hours.

Pinwheels with Black Bean Filling

¾ cup cooked black beans or 8 ounce can

1 (3 ounce) cream cheese, softened

2 teaspoons jalapeño peppers, finely diced

½ medium sweet red pepper, finely diced

8 (6 inch) flour tortillas

1 cup white Cheddar cheese, shredded

1 bunch green onions, finely diced

Salsa and guacamole

In medium mixing bowl, mash ½ cup black beans. Stir in remaining beans, cream cheese, and jalapeño peppers. Spread tortilla with black bean mixture, sprinkle with shredded Cheddar cheese, red pepper, and onions. Roll up tightly. Wrap in plastic wrap and chill 4 to 8 hours. Remove plastic wrap and slice ½-¾ inch thick slices. Place on platter; serve with salsa or guacamole.

Sausage and Mushroom Dip

1 pound Italian sausage, browned and drained

1 tablespoon cooking oil

8 ounces mushrooms, sliced

½ cup onion, chopped

½ cup sweet pepper, chopped

1 (8 ounce) package cream cheese, softened

½ teaspoon Worcestershire sauce

Assorted crackers

Brown and drain sausage. Set aside. Remove drippings from skillet. In skillet heat oil and cook mushrooms, onions, and peppers until tender. In bowl, blend cream cheese and Worcestershire sauce. Add cream cheese to vegetable mixture, heat until cream cheese is melted. Add sausage and stir. Transfer to chafing dish and serve warm with crackers.

Bacon Wrapped Smokies

1 (14 ounce) package Lil Smokies

15 slices of uncooked bacon, cut into thirds

¾ cup brown sugar

½ teaspoon cayenne pepper

Preheat oven to 375°F. Line a rimmed baking sheet (jellyroll pan) with parchment paper or foil. Wrap each smokie with a strip of bacon, overlapping at ends and secure with a toothpick. In a shallow bowl, mix brown sugar and cayenne pepper. Firmly press each bacon-wrapped smokie into brown sugar mixture coating generously. Place a single layer on prepared baking sheet seam side down. Bake for 15-20 minutes or until bacon is browned. Rotate each link and bake for an additional 15-20 minutes until bacon is browned on both sides. Serve warm.

Blue Cheese Ball

1 (8 ounce) package cream cheese, softened

1 (4 ounce) container Blue cheese, crumbled

½ cup ripe olives, chopped

1 teaspoon Worcestershire sauce

1 cup pecans, finely chopped

In mixing bowl, combine the first 4 ingredients, mixing until blended. Shape into a ball, using wet hands. Roll cheese ball in pecans. Cover and chill thoroughly. Serves: 8-10. Note: If anyone is allergic to pecans, substitute with nut of choice.

SETTING
a Formal Table

The key to setting a formal table is to set it in such a way that you will not intimidate your guests. Cater your setting to match the various courses served. A general rule is no more than three knives, three forks, and a spoon should be initially placed on the table. This is known as the Rule of Three. This will help prevent a cluttered table. If the meal requires additional utensils, they should be brought out with their respective dishes. The stemware should be limited to four glasses per person. Coffee may be served individually as the meal progresses.

A FORMAL MENU

APPETIZER: Phyllo Cheese Tarts
MAIN DISH: Grilled Beef Tenderloin with Mushroom Sauce
SIDE DISHES: Mashed Red Potatoes and Roasted Asparagus with Peppers
DESSERT: Chocolate Hazelnut Torte
MENU RECIPES:

Phyllo Cheese Tarts

2 (2.1 ounce) packages frozen mini phyllo pastry shells, thawed

1 cup cottage cheese, low-fat

1 large egg, lightly beaten

¼ cup Parmesan cheese, grated

1 teaspoon Italian seasoning

Preheat oven to 350°F. Place pastry shells in ungreased mini muffin pans; set aside. In medium bowl, combine remaining ingredients. Spoon mixture into shells. Bake for 20 minutes or until centers are firm. **Garnish:** Commercial pesto sauce or diced pimento.

Grilled Beef Tenderloin with Mushroom Sauce

1 (6 pound) beef tenderloin, trimmed

3 tablespoons coarse ground black pepper

1 (10 ounce) bottle white-wine Worcestershire sauce for chicken

1 recipe favorite mushroom sauce (if desired)

Rub tenderloin with pepper. Place tenderloin in a shallow dish or heavy-duty zipper-lock plastic bag; add Worcestershire. Cover or seal, and chill for at least 3 hours. Preheat grill to medium-high heat (350°F to 400°F). Remove tenderloin from bag and discard marinade. Grill tenderloin, covered with lid, over direct heat for 10 minutes, turning once. Reduce heat to medium-low (250°F to 300°F), and grill, covered with lid for 40 minutes, or until desired degree of doneness, turning every 10 minutes. Remove from grill. Cover loosely with aluminum foil, and let stand for 15 minutes before slicing. Serve with mushroom sauce. Yields: 12 servings.

Mashed Red Potatoes

10 cups unpeeled and cubed red potatoes (about 5 pounds)

5 tablespoons butter

¼ cup milk or half and half

½ cup sour cream

1½ teaspoons salt

½ teaspoon ground pepper

In a large saucepan, combine potatoes and add water to cover. Boil over high heat for approximately 15 minutes, or until potatoes are tender. In large bowl, combine hot potatoes and remaining ingredients. Stir with a spoon until blended and potatoes are coarsely mashed. Yields: 12 servings.

Roasted Asparagus with Peppers

3 tablespoons olive oil

2 garlic cloves, minced

1 teaspoon fresh thyme, chopped

Salt and Pepper

1 pound medium asparagus, ends removed

1 red or yellow pepper, thinly sliced

4 shallots, thinly sliced

1 tablespoon red wine vinegar

Preheat oven to 450°F. Stir oil, garlic, thyme, 1 teaspoon salt, and ½ teaspoon pepper together in a bowl. Trim asparagus and spread across rimmed baking sheet; drizzle with half of the garlic mixture and toss to coat. Rearrange asparagus in single rows. Combine sliced pepper and shallots with remaining garlic mixture in bowl and toss to coat. Scatter pepper and shallots evenly over asparagus. Roast for 10 minutes until asparagus begins to soften and turns bright green with some dark edges. Drizzle with vinegar and continue to roast until asparagus begins to soften and peppers and shallots are beginning to turn golden brown around edges. Toss vegetables, season with salt and pepper. Yields: 4 Servings.

Chocolate Hazelnut Torte

1½ cups hazelnuts

2 tablespoons all-purpose flour

2 tablespoons sugar

⅓ cup butter, softened

Preheat oven to 350°F. Process hazelnuts in a food processor until finely chopped. Add remaining ingredients, pulsing until mixture holds together. Press into the bottom of 9-inch spring form pan. Bake for 10 minutes. Remove from oven, and set aside while preparing filling. Keep oven on.

FILLING:

1 cup butter, divided

3 (4 ounces) bittersweet chocolate baking bars, broken into 1-inch pieces

1¾ cups sugar

6 large eggs, separated

1 cup all-purpose flour

In a small microwave-safe bowl, melt ¼ cup butter and chocolate pieces on high in 30-second intervals until melted. <u>Note</u>: Approximately 1½ minutes. Stir until smooth. Set aside to cool. In large bowl, beat remaining ¾ cup butter and sugar at medium speed until fluffy. Add egg yolks, one at a time, beating well after each addition. Stir in flour and melted chocolate. In a separate bowl, beat egg whites at high speed with an electric mixer until stiff peaks form. Fold egg whites into chocolate mixture. Spoon batter into prepared crust. Bake for 1 hour. Cool for 1 hour. Refrigerate for 4 hours before serving. Garnish with whipped cream and berries. Yields: One 9-inch torte.

SETTING
a Casual Table

The casual setting is designed for everyday use and features basic dinnerware, glassware, and utensils. Both formal and casual settings follow the same basic format. In the center is the dinner plate, with or without a charger. It is placed directly in front of the guest's seat. Forks are placed to the left of the plate, and spoons and knives to the right. The knife blade should be facing inward toward the edge of the dinner plate with the spoon on it's right. Once those basic things are done, the rest of the utensils should simply suit the occasion and menu.

A CASUAL MENU

APPETIZER: Black-eyed Pea Salsa

MAIN DISH: Cheesy Tortilla Casserole

DESSERT: Chocolate Chip Cookies and
Homemade Buttery Pecan Ice Cream

MENU RECIPES:

Black-eyed Pea Salsa and Chips

3 (15.8 ounce) cans black-eyed peas

1 (10 ounce) can diced tomatoes
with green chilies

1 cup cilantro, chopped

1 small onion, finely chopped

1 jalapeño pepper, seeded and minced

2 cloves garlic, minced

1 teaspoon salt

½ teaspoon ground black pepper

2 tablespoons olive oil

In a large bowl, combine first eight ingredients. Toss gently with olive oil. Serve with Cumin Pita Chips.
Yields: 6 cups

Cheesy Tortilla Casserole

1 (28 ounce) can diced tomatoes, drained

1 small onion, diced

2 garlic cloves, peeled

2 canned chipotle chilies

2 tablespoons olive oil

2 cups rotisserie chicken, shredded

¾ cup low-sodium chicken broth

¼ cup fresh cilantro, chopped

Salt and pepper

15 (5-inch) tostados or 8 cups corn tortilla chips,
broken

1½ cups Monterey Jack cheese, shredded

1 cup sour cream, for topping

Preheat oven to 425°F. Grease 2-quart casserole dish. Puree tomatoes, onion, garlic, and chilis in blender until smooth. Heat oil in medium saucepan over medium heat until simmering. Add tomato sauce, bring to simmer, and cook until slightly thickened, 5 to 7 minutes. Add chicken, broth, and cilantro and season with salt and pepper to taste. Place half of chips in prepared dish, top with half sauce and chicken mixture and half of cheese. Repeat second layer. Be sure a few chips are exposed so they can crisp while cooking. Bake until bubbly and cheese is golden brown, 15 to 20 minutes. Top servings with sour cream. Yields: 4 servings.

Chocolate Chip Cookies

2¼ cups all-purpose flour

1 teaspoon baking soda

½ teaspoon salt

1 cup butter, softened

1 cup granulated sugar

1 cup light brown sugar, firmly packed

2 teaspoons vanilla extract

2 large eggs, room temperature

2 cups semisweet chocolate chips

1 cup walnuts or pecans, chopped

Preheat oven 350°F. Combine flour, baking soda, and salt; set aside. In large mixing bowl, beat butter with sugars at medium speed until creamy. Add vanilla and eggs, one at a time, and mix on low speed until incorporated. Gradually blend dry ingredients into creamed mixture. Stir in chocolate chips and nuts. Drop by tablespoons onto ungreased cookie sheet. Bake for 9 to 11 minutes or until golden brown.

Homemade Buttery Pecan Ice Cream

¾ cup light brown sugar, firmly packed

½ cup water

⅛ teaspoon salt

2 large eggs, lightly beaten

2 tablespoons butter

1 cup half and half

1 teaspoon vanilla extract

1 cup whipping cream

½ cup pecans, toasted and chopped

Combine brown sugar, water, and salt in a double boiler; bringing water in the bottom to a boil. Reduce heat to low; cook and stir brown sugar mixture 3 to 4 minutes or until sugar dissolves. Gradually stir in 2 tablespoons of hot mixture into eggs; add eggs to remaining hot mixture, stirring constantly. Cook over medium heat, stirring until thermometer reads 160°F and the mixture thickens, approximately 4 to 5 minutes. Remove from heat; stir in butter and cool. Stir in half and half and remaining ingredients. Pour into a 2-quart freezer container, either hand-crank or electric. Follow manufacturer's instructions. Note: For firmer ice cream, pack freezer with additional ice and rock salt; let stand an hour before serving. If you do not have a double boiler, make your own. Fill a saucepan with 2 inches of water before beginning. Place a large, Pyrex glass mixing bowl over large saucepan. Be sure the glass bowl fits snuggly atop the pan. The bowl should not be touching the water. Follow directions above. Yields: 1 quart.

RAHAB
A Woman of Great Faith

Biblical Principle: Those who seek humbly after God, in faith, will be saved.

Read Joshua Chapters 1, 2, and 6.

1. In whose home did the spies take refuge? What was so unusual about this woman?

2. Joshua 2:9 is a beautiful statement of faith made by Rahab. She acknowledged God as the God of the heavens and the earth. Have you come to the place in your life where you have acknowledged God as the God of the heavens and the earth, and the God of your life? Tell about it.

3. What did the spies tell Rahab she was to do before their return, and what would they do for her if she followed their commands?

4. Read Hebrews Chapter 11. Why do you think Rahab made the Bible's Faith Hall of Fame?

5. Do you have a faith that would make you eligible for the Bible's Faith Hall of Fame? What would qualify you?

6. What lessons have you learned from Rahab that you can apply to your life?

What I Learned Today

Week Nine

COUPLE'S DATE NIGHT

A KISS OR A HANDSHAKE

*T*he first date Mark and I had was attending a Christian concert on his college campus. I was so excited after his call. My mind filled with questions, such as what was I going to wear? I wanted to make a good impression; after all, he was a junior in college and here I was just a sophomore in high school. This was a big deal! I thought long and hard about my outfit and how I was going to wear my hair. The big night came and with it lots of butterflies, all flying in a circular formation in my stomach. I had only dated one other young man, so my experience with dating was limited, especially when it came to college guys!

Mark arrived looking very handsome; *fine* would be a better word. I had observed him from a distance for several months, and he was always nicely dressed. His shoes were freshly polished, and he was wearing the latest fashion. We went out to dinner and on to the concert. It was a fun evening; we found that we had a lot to talk about. Once we arrived to my house, I invited him in, but he politely declined. With a warm handshake, the evening was over. The next day, he called and we talked for a long time. In the weeks to follow, we had several dates, all ending in a polite, warm handshake followed by, "Dianne, I really had a good time tonight." Now, I was young and inexperienced at dating, but I thought a kiss meant he had a good time. What did a warm handshake mean? I was a little confused!

*A*fter a few months, it came—the kiss! I could then ask what I'd wanted to ask him for weeks: "Why did you wait so long?" He explained that he and a friend had agreed that neither of them would kiss a girl after a certain number of dates, just to see what she would do. They challenged each other as to whether or not the young woman would hang around. They called it, "The Florida Challenge"—both being from South Florida. I guess you have to be a guy to understand that one!

We can all look back on our dating years; for some, it hasn't been very long ago and for others it has been quite some time. Why is dating a *priority* before we marry and not a *priority* afterwards? Perhaps, it's because before we marry, the guy is trying to *catch* the girl and of course, she wants to be *caught*. What about now that you're married? It would seem that the longer a couple is married the less they make dating a priority. After all, he's got her now!

As the years go by, there are careers to consider, the purchase of a first home, children being born, job changes, and then the purchase of the second home—bigger than the first—requiring additional bills and extra responsibility. The cost of a baby sitter is far more than you can afford, the finances are tight, and on and on. Perhaps there are many reasons or *excuses* for not dating your spouse, but spending time alone with your spouse is necessary for keeping the oneness in your relationship. A date night can spark communication, uninterrupted communication, and cause you both to remember what drew you to one another in the first place. We, as your Secrets leadership, want to give you this date night in hopes that it will be a reminder to you and your spouse of how important it is to make date nights a priority in your marriage relationship. Enjoy!

Marriage BOOK LIST

- *A Lifelong Love* by Gary Thomas
- *As Long as We Both Shall Live* by Gary Smalley and Ted Cunningham
- *Boundaries in Marriage* by Dr. Henry Cloud and Dr. John Townsend
- *Cherish* by Gary Thomas
- *Created to Be His Help Meet* by Debi Pearl
- *Devotions for a Sacred Marriage* by Gary Thomas
- *Every Man's Marriage* by Stephen Arterburn and Fred Stocker
- *Have a New Husband by Friday* by Dr. Kevin Leman
- *Hidden Keys of a Loving and Lasting Marriage* by Gary Smalley
- *His Needs—Her Needs* by Willard F. Harley
- *Intended for Pleasure* by Ed Wheat, M.D. and Kaye Wheat
- *Intimacy Ignited* by Linda Dillow
- *Intimate Issues* by Linda Dillow
- *Love and Respect for a Lifetime* by Dr. Emerson Eggerichs
- *Love and War* by John Eldredge and Stasi Eldredge
- *Marriage on the Rock* by Jimmy Evans
- *Momentary Marriage* by John Piper
- *Night Light* by Dr. James and Shirley Dobson
- *Passages of Marriage* by Frank and Mary Minirith
- *Pray Big for Your Marriage* by Will Davis Jr.
- *Quiet Times for Couples* by H. Norm Wright
- *Romantic Lovers* by David and Carol Hocking
- *Sacred Marriage* by Gary Thomas
- *Sheet Music* by Dr. Kevin Leman
- *The Act of Marriage* by Tim and Beverly LaHaye
- *The 8 Love Languages* by Gary Chapman
- *The Excellent Wife* by Martha Pierce
- *The Four Seasons of Marriage: Secrets to a Lasting Marriage* by Gary Chapman
- *The Love Dare* by Stephen Kendrick
- *What's It Like to Be Married to Me?* by Linda Dillow
- *Young and in Love* by Ted Cunningham

CREATIVE STAY-AT-HOME DATES [16]

*M*ost of our date nights are at home, so bedtime for the kids on date night is strict; they go down at 7:00. They can read in bed until 8:00, but they may not get up except to go to the bathroom. It took a little effort for them to get into the habit, but they have learned, and it's been good.

We always feed the kids early and then we enjoy a meal together. Sometimes our whole date revolves around the meal. My husband loves to cook, and I enjoy being in the kitchen with him. So sometimes we cook something extra special and the cooking process is the date. We have done fondue, made different breads, and made homemade egg rolls; we've just been creative. Usually, though, the meal is something simple; frequently it's a junk food meal, just because we can! When we were still in the Memphis area, a couple of times we did take-out from a favorite restaurant.

Our most common activities are movies, sports on TV, games, or just having a good talk. We also work a puzzle now and then, although that's not as much my husband's thing. But we've also done fun home projects together. We spent two or three date nights in a row once building our own bookshelves. We had such fun! More than once, we've spent date night either plotting or implementing the rearrangement of a room (we both love to rearrange furniture), or building new music playlists for our iPod can be a fun thing to do as well. We've also done really crazy things like design our dream house or spend the evening plotting how we'd spend an exorbitant amount of money. We've done more serious things like talking through potential changes in our lives or dreams that we have.

One idea we had that we were never able to implement this past summer was to actually find a babysitter, pack a picnic supper, and go to the pool or lake. We had access to a friend's pool, and we would have been able to swim, just the two of us, and have a free meal; the only expense would have been the babysitter. We never did work out the implementation of that possibility.

There is always the most expected date night activity—sex. But to be honest, we frequently leave *that* out of date night. Although that's a very important part of our relationship, we don't want that to *be* what dating each other is about. So we frequently specifically plan *that* for other nights and only spend date night that way once every few weeks. That would be different for other couples, I'm sure; that's just how we approach it.

Having to come up with things that make date night special and unique compared to every other night of the week has taught us a few things about each other. It has not been about me doing things my husband likes one week and him reciprocating the next. It has been about us learning more and more how much we have in common, like how many movies we truly enjoy together. Many activities I thought were primarily my interest are truly exciting for him as well. We love it when we discover that new favorite board game, an unexpected great movie that has us discussing it for a while afterward, or that new activity that we'd never even thought of before. Just be creative and have fun together.

By Ann B. Hibbard

[16] Ann B. Hibbard, "Creative Stay-at-Home Date Nights" (Secrets Savored Leader Guide, 2012).

FAVORITE DATES

- A daytime date! Go to a local park for a picnic or take in a matinee movie.

- Going to a fondue restaurant and cooking our own dinner. Most meals from start to finish take a couple of hours; it's a great time to enjoy good conversation with my spouse. To make this more budget friendly, have a fondue night at home!

- Going to a bookstore and just moseying around the books and magazines, grabbing some coffee while we're there, and just picking up a good read and hanging out together.

- Going to the mall and stopping in Brookstone® to play with all of the expensive gadgets. It's fun to walk around the mall and just people watch, pretending to buy stuff you can't afford as newlyweds.

- Taking a drive through an expensive neighborhood to look at the beautiful homes and landscape.

- Daycation to a nearby city. Leaving home for a full day of exploring another city close by.

- A bike ride to a close restaurant.

- Take a trip to the dog park.

- Date night to the fair/circus.

- 3D movies are always fun!

- Make dinner together. My husband picks out what he wants to eat then we go and get all of the ingredients together and cook up something delish.

- Frozen yogurt date—competition to see who gets the most froyo

- Playing at Best Buy—watching TV, playing video games, sitting in the theater room, and looking at all the fancy appliances. This is good, inexpensive fun.

- Go grab a Redbox® movie, some take out, and have dinner and a movie at home.

- We love finding a restaurant outside of town, like a catfish place, and driving out to have dinner, then going for yogurt or ice cream once back in town and finally home. We do not want to arrive before the sitter has the children in bed; after all, that is part of the reason we have a sitter! Having the drive time gives us time to talk without interruptions, as long as we both put our cells on silent!

- We love to ride our bikes on the Greenline from the suburb to downtown and have breakfast at a new restaurant.

- Taking a drive in the country and finding unique antique/junk stores to explore.

- We like to go strawberry picking in the summer at an agricultural park in our city and pumpkin patch exploring in the fall at a local farm.

What I Learned Today

Things I cherish about my husband ...

Things I cherish about my wife ...

Week Nine

GIRL'S NIGHT OUT

COLLEGE AND SINGLE
Young Women

*T*onight is a special night in which your leadership wants to honor you with dinner and dessert. The introductory story of how Mark and I began our dating years is one that I hope you enjoyed reading. I have found that God works uniquely different in the lives of all His children. For me, God gave me my mate for life at a young age. I am grateful for many reasons, but mainly because Mark was diagnosed at the age of 56 with a rare condition that drastically changed our lives and our marriage. I am thankful that we were able to begin our relationship at such a young age and have the years we had before Mark became ill and subsequently passed away at the age of 67.

Perhaps you are in high school, college, or single. No matter where you are, you can rest in knowing that God knows the mate He has chosen for you and in the right time, He will bring your lives together. His plans, His ways, and His timing are always perfect. So, relax and trust Him. I was blessed to find my mate at a young age, but I know of numerous young women who were willing to wait, no matter their age, and God gave them a wonderful mate in which to share their lives. Waiting on God brings about the best for your life; do not settle for anything but God's best!

Many Are the Plans

I came to an understanding years ago, that "Many are the plans in a man's heart, but it's the Lord's purpose that prevails." Proverbs 19:21

I began at the early age of eight striving to determine the plans for my life. At this point, I was determined to be a detective and take my place as the fourth angel on *Charlie's Angels*. By age twelve, I was going to be a news anchorwoman. I sat for hours in the bathroom with my round brush, practicing my "and now for our local weather" voice.

Next up were my high school years. It was in that season of life that I realized I had a flare for teaching. My former third-grade teacher permitted me to "teach" a few lessons every week for a short period of time when I was her teacher's aide. It was then that I found my calling. I proceeded down the road of elementary education and started striving to set my life plans in order.

At eighteen years of age, I began college. I was determined to get my degree, a job, followed by marriage, then have children and enjoy summers off for family vacations. Well, I did end up with a fun job teaching first grade. I truly loved it, but I was still missing several parts of *my plan*—husband, children, and family vacations!

Fortunately, while in college, I had the privilege of being discipled! Through that experience, I realized that single or married, God had called me to invest my life in others. So, I began striving to do that anytime I felt God had opened a door. I went on many youth trips as a counselor, spent summers working for BREAKAWAY Ministries, mentored girls at the Big Oak Girls Ranch, and found complete joy in living out 2 Timothy 2:2. I absolutely loved being able to teach and disciple others what God had so graciously taught me through those who had discipled me.

Unfortunately, I was still lonely for my life mate. I remember praying and crying many nights and telling God, despite the loneliness, "I choose You!" I remember watching friend after friend get married and have children. The loneliness some days seemed unbearable. And yet, it pushed me to the feet of Jesus and made me cling to His Word for hope and security. I learned I had to be intentional in my walk with the Lord, and so I sought to strive to do whatever I could not to fall prey to the ways of the world.

As time went on, God truly proved His faithfulness in my life. I laugh at the fact that I can quote nearly all the verses in the Bible on "waiting." I will tell you now that without a doubt, God's timing is Worth the Wait!

I met the most amazing man at thirty-six years of age and married him one month before my thirty-eighth birthday. Now, at the age of forty-two, I am a mother to the cutest, most adorable little boy ever, and I can confidently say that God's timing is perfect! He is trustworthy, faithful, and HE KNOWS THE PLANS HE HAS FOR YOU!

by Leslie Hollowell

Girl Time

- Flannel Night—Rent a girl flick and have friends over; everyone comes in their flannels. Pop popcorn and have a variety of candy on hand.

- Bake Night—Girls come with their favorite recipe, including the ingredients. Spend the night in the kitchen baking, then divide goods to go home with each girl who participated.

- Caroling—Get a group of friends together and go caroling, then back to your apartment for hot chocolate.

- Giving—You and several friends can adopt a family for Christmas. Take a Saturday before Christmas, meet for breakfast, and then shop together. Go back to your place, wrap all the gifts and then deliver them.

- Hit the Rafts—Go white water rafting with a group of friends.

- Pray—Start a prayer group with some friends who are as desiring as you are for God to bring you the right mate. Meet once a month to pray.

- Mocha Latte Night—Have friends over for a variety of coffee drinks. Everyone brings a different flavoring for the coffee.

- Picnic—Go for a picnic at the park with friends. Have a Frisbee throwing contest, giving ribbons or prizes for the furthest throw, the shortest throw, the fanciest throw, the most unique throw, the most pitiful throw, etc.

- Pinterest Party—Each guest brings an idea and the supplies to make a craft found on Pinterest. Prepare one or two recipes to serve that you found on Pinterest.

- A Play and Dessert—Go with a group of friends to a play and out for dessert. Try a buggy or horse-drawn carriage ride downtown.

- Painting Party—Need a room in your apartment painted? Have a painting party. If you feed them, they will paint for you! Have a contest as to who can come with the most creative painting attire.

- Breakfast Out—Make memories by taking your nieces or nephews out to breakfast every once in a while; they will love it!

- Watermelon—Have a watermelon carving contest at a picnic with friends. Give prizes for the funniest, the most creative, etc.

- Sports Anyone?—Start a recreational volleyball team with friends. Many public parks have outdoor volleyball courts.

- Spa Day—Have a Girls' Spa Day and ask several of your friends to go with you to get a manicure and pedicure, then out to lunch. Or if money is tight, give manicures and pedicures to one another.

- Write it Down—Journal your way through high school, college, and beyond. You will be amazed years later as you read back through your journals all that God taught you during that time.

- Bikes Anyone?—Take a bike ride through a local park with friends.

- Venture Out—Try a new restaurant with a friend in a remote part of town where you have never been.

- Daytime Travel—Take a day trip with friends to a city—within three to four hours—for shopping, sightseeing, or trying out a new restaurant.

- Serving—Commit one day a month to do a good deed for someone else.

- Adopt—Gather a few friends and adopt a widow. Take her to dinner once a month and celebrate her birthday each year with a party.

- Garden Party—Each spring invite a friend over to help plant a box garden or plant flowers in the yard. Prepare a special lunch.

BOOKS FOR *Her*

- *A Lifetime of Wisdom* by Joni Eareckson Tada
- *A Loving Life* by Paul E. Miller
- *A Praying Life* by Paul E. Miller
- *A Young Woman After God's Own Heart*
  by Elizabeth George
- *A Young Woman's Guide to Making Right Decisions*
  by Elizabeth George
- *A Young Woman's Walk with God: Growing More Like Jesus*
  by Elizabeth George
- *Before Amen* by Max Lucado
- *Courtesy and Kindness for Young Ladies* by Emilie Barnes
- *Every Young Woman's Battle: Guarding Your Mind*
  by Shannon Ethridge and Stephen Arterburn
- *Fresh Wind Fresh Fire* by Jim Cymbala
- *Heart's Cry* by Jennifer Kennedy Dean
- *Kisses from Katie* by Katie Davis Major
- *Let Me Be a Woman* by Elizabeth Elliott
- *Lies Young Women Believe* by Nancy Leigh DeMoss
- *Live a Praying Life* by Jennifer Kennedy Dean
- *Spiritual Disciplines for the Christian Life* by Donald S. Whitney
- *Simplify Your Spiritual Life* by Donald S. Whitney
- *The Hiding Place* by Corrie tin Boom
- *The Indwelling Life of Christ* by Major W. Ian Thomas
- *The Red Sea Rules* by Robert J. Morgan
- *The Release of the Spirit* by Watchman Nee
- *Twelve Extraordinary Women* by John MacArthur
- *Waiting on God* by Andrew Murray

What I Learned Today

Week Ten

A HOLIDAY TO REMEMBER

CREATIVE HOLIDAY DECORATING
AND GIFT GIVING

*T*his session is designed to provide the young women with ideas for decorating and gift giving on a limited budget. The holiday season comes with a great deal of stress, and much of the stress is a result of the expenses and extra commitments that occur.

In an effort to help alleviate the stress of spending and shopping, invite several guests to share ideas on decorating and gift giving. Invite women known for their creativity to come and demonstrate some fun and creative ways in which the young women can make their own gifts and Christmas decorations.

Example:

- Hands-on instruction showing how fresh greenery can be used to make wreaths and swags for doors or used in table arrangements.

- Instructions can be given for making Christmas ornaments and tree decorations.

- Party ideas can be shared, such as, having a birthday party for Jesus, and how to use this opportunity to share the gospel at Christmas.

- Ideas can be shared for creating meaningful gifts to be given to family and friends. Example: Shadow box a special art work done by you as a child to give a parent. If there is an old handwritten letter given by a family member who has past that would be special to your parents, frame it for them for Christmas.

- If time permits, allow the young women to create their own gifts and décor for the holidays.

Encourage the participants to bring a friend to class this week. Leadership will provide a prepared dish or baked good—one of their favorite Christmas recipes to be enjoyed by the class and guests. Hostess will provide coffee and beverage.

Note: If you have more than one Secrets Savored class in your church, you may want to offer this in the evening and combine classes, meeting at the church or in a large home.

Thanksgiving Treasures

Give thanks with a grateful heart; give thanks to the Holy One. Give thanks because He's given Jesus Christ, God's Son. And now, let the weak say, 'I am strong,' let the poor say, 'I am rich, because of what the Lord has done for us,' Give thanks, give thanks."[17] Song by Marantha! Music

---

FAMILY BLESSINGS AND FAMILY FUN

Take time as a family to reflect on God's blessings from the past year. A Basket Full of Blessings is a wonderful way for your family to recount, not only God's blessings, but the blessings of each family member. A very small wicker basket is placed at each family member's place setting and at the place of each guest. Place a large basket in the center of the table containing small strips of paper and pens. On Thanksgiving Day, prior to the meal, each family member and guest will use the strips of paper to write a blessing or Thanksgiving remembrance to each person, placing it in the respective baskets. After the prayer is said, before the meal is served (or after the meal), each person reads their little basket full of blessings. It is a vivid illustration of how we need to encourage and bless one another.

"Oh give thanks to the Lord, for He is good! For His mercy endures forever."
1 Chronicles 16:34, NKJV[18]

"In everything give thanks; for this is the will of God in Christ Jesus for you."
1 Thessalonians 5:18, NKJV[19]

WREATH

Begin with a florist foam ring and soak overnight in water. Stand it in the sink to drain thoroughly; once soaked, the flowers will stay fresher longer. To make a sun flower wreath, run florist wire through the back of three sunflower seed heads, and attach in a triangular pattern. Push the flower stems—cut to three to four inches below the bloom—into the foam, filling out the arrangement. Place a bow on the wreath and hang on front door for a fall welcome to guests. Wreaths can also be used as a centerpiece with a chunky candle in the center.

INDIAN CORN GARLAND

Construct an easy-to-assemble Indian corn garland beginning with sisal rope. Dye it a dark brown or a golden maze color. Wrap it with broomcorn, corn tassels (found at Farmer's Markets), or other dried grasses. Place corn along the rope in a single row or gathered in bunches of three. Wire corn securely in place, and then tie raffia on top for a festive finishing touch. Hang garland from your front door or across your mantel.

---

[17] Maranatha, *Praise 10: O Lord, My Lord.*
[18] Charles Stanley, *The Charles F. Stanley Life Principles Bible: New King James Version* (Thomas Nelson Publishing, 2005).
[19] Charles Stanley, *The Charles F. Stanley Life Principles Bible: New King James Version* (Thomas Nelson Publishing, 2005).

FALL RECIPES

Apple and Spice Sugar Glazed Turkey

1 (12 pound) turkey

¼ cup brown sugar, firmly packed

2 tablespoons kosher salt

1½ teaspoons onion powder

1 teaspoon garlic powder

2 teaspoons allspice

½ teaspoon ground cloves

½ teaspoon mace

1 large onion, quartered

2 (14 ounce) chicken broth, additional broth

2 tablespoons all-purpose flour

GARNISHES: fresh rosemary sprigs, apple slices, nuts

Preheat oven to 325°F. Remove giblets and neck. Rinse turkey thoroughly, pat dry. Tie legs together with kitchen twine; tuck wingtips under. Combine brown sugar and next six ingredients. Rub over turkey. Cover and chill 8 hours. Place turkey on a rack in a roasting pan, breast side up. Arrange onion quarters around turkey. Pour two cans of broth in bottom of pan. Bake loosely covered with foil for 1½ hours. Uncover and bake 1½ additional hours or until thermometer registers 180°F. Cover with foil to avoid excessive browning. Remove onions and discard; reserve drippings. Let turkey stand 15 minutes before carving. Combine drippings and enough broth to equal 2 cups in a saucepan over medium heat. Whisk in 2 tablespoons flour and cook, whisking constantly for about 5 minutes until thickened. Serve with turkey.

Baked Sweet Mashed Potatoes

3½ pounds baking potatoes, peeled, cut in 1-inch pieces

1 tablespoon salt, divided

1 (29 ounce) can sweet potatoes in syrup, drained and mashed

¼ cup butter

1 (8 ounce) package cream cheese, softened

6 bacon slices, cooked and crumbled

¾ cup chicken broth

¾ cup sour cream

1 teaspoon pepper

Preheat oven to 350°F. Bring potatoes, ½ tablespoon salt, and water to a boil in Dutch oven for thirty minutes, or until tender. Drain. Return potatoes to pan. Add sweet potatoes, butter, and cream cheese; mash until smooth with a potato masher. Stir in bacon, next three ingredients, and remaining ½ tablespoon salt. Spoon mixture into a lightly greased 9x13 dish. Bake uncovered for 25 minutes.

Make Ahead Turkey Gravy

2 turkey necks

2 tablespoons canola oil

1 medium onion, coarsely chopped

1 celery rib, coarsely chopped

5 cups chicken broth, or pan drippings

¼ cup fresh flat-leafed parsley, chopped

1 fresh thyme sprig

4 tablespoons butter

¼ to ½ cup all-purpose flour

½ teaspoon rubbed sage

Salt and pepper to taste

Brown turkey neck in hot oil over medium heat 2 to 3 minutes on each side. Add onion and celery; sauté 5 minutes. Stir in broth, parsley, and thyme. Bring to a boil and reduce heat. Simmer, stirring occasionally, for 30 minutes. Pour through a wire-mesh strainer; discard solids. Melt butter in large skillet, and whisk in flour until smooth. Cook, whisking constantly for 4 to 5 minutes until golden brown. Gradually whisk in stock (or pan drippings), and sage; bring to a boil over medium heat. Reduce heat and simmer, stirring occasionally for 5 to 10 minutes or until thickened. Salt and pepper to taste.

Brussels Sprouts with Apples

2¼ pounds fresh Brussels sprouts, halved

2 tablespoons fresh lemon juice

2 teaspoons salt, divided

¼ cup butter, divided

½ medium onion, diced

¼ cup apple juice

1 large red delicious apple, diced

1 garlic clove, minced

2 teaspoons sugar

1 (8 ounce) can sliced chestnuts, drained

½ cup golden raisins

2 teaspoons lemon rind, grated

½ teaspoon ground pepper

½ teaspoon ground nutmeg

In saucepan, bring Brussels sprouts, lemon juice, 1½ teaspoon salt, and water to a boil. Cover, reduce heat, and simmer 5 to 10 minutes or until tender. Drain and keep warm. Melt 2 tablespoons butter in large skillet over medium-high heat; add onion and sauté 15 to 20 minutes or until caramel colored. Add apple juice and cook 2 minutes, stirring to loosen browned particles. Add apple, garlic, and sugar. Cook, stirring constantly for 5 to 6 minutes or until apple is tender. Add water chestnuts and next four ingredients, remaining ½ teaspoon salt, and remaining 2 tablespoons butter. Cook, stirring constantly for 3 to 4 minutes. Gently toss in Brussels sprouts.

Green Beans with Roquefort Cheese and Walnuts

1 pound fresh green beans, trimmed

1 (4 ounce) Roquefort cheese, crumbled

1 cup walnuts, toasted

½ teaspoon salt

½ teaspoon ground pepper

5 thick bacon slices, cut ¼-inch pieces

Place green beans in saucepan, covered with water, simmer for 3 minutes, until crisp-tender. Drain and rinse with cold water. Set aside. In skillet, cook bacon until crisp. Drain on paper towel, reserve drippings. Sauté green beans in hot drippings in skillet 2 minutes or until heated. Sprinkle with cheese and cook, stirring constantly for 30 seconds or just until cheese begins to melt. Sprinkle evenly with walnuts, salt, pepper, and bacon. Serve immediately.

Cornbread Stuffing

¾ cup butter

2 large celery stalks with leaves, chopped to 1½ cups

¾ cup onion, finely diced

9 cups prepared cornbread, cubed

1 teaspoon dried thyme

2 teaspoons sage

1 teaspoon poultry seasoning

Salt and pepper to taste

Preheat oven to 350°F. Melt butter in Dutch oven over medium heat. Cook celery and onions until tender. Remove from heat. In large bowl, toss celery mixture and remaining ingredients. Place in 9x13 baking dish. Bake covered for approximately 30 minutes. Remove foil and bake additional 15 minutes until golden brown.

Perfect Pecan Pie

1 (15 ounce) package refrigerated piecrust (should include two crusts)

3 large eggs, room temperature

1 cup sugar

¾ cup corn syrup

4 tablespoons butter, melted

1 tablespoon vanilla

½ teaspoon salt

1½ cups pecan halves

Preheat oven to 350°F. Remove crusts from package and gently roll and press together for a thick crust. Fit into a 9-inch pie plate; fold edges under and crimp. Stir together eggs and next five ingredients; mix well. Stir in pecans. Pour filling into crust and bake for 55 minutes or until set. Serve warm with vanilla ice cream.

Chestnut Chocolate Tassies

1 (10 ounce) package frozen puff pastry shells, thawed

½ pound whole chestnuts, shelled (1½ cups)

1 cup sugar

1 cup milk or half and half

1 (6 ounce) semisweet chocolate baking bar, coarsely chopped

2 tablespoons rum flavor

1¼ cups heavy cream, whipped

Chocolate shavings

Prepare pastry shells according to package. Bring chestnuts, sugar, and milk to a boil in a saucepan, stir until sugar dissolves. Reduce heat and simmer 30 minutes or until chestnuts are tender and mixture thickens. Microwave chocolate in glass bowl at high for 30 seconds, until melted, stirring once. Remove chestnut mixture from heat; add in chocolate and rum flavoring. Process chestnut mixture in food processor, 1 cup at a time, until smooth. Cool completely. Beat cream at low with mixer for 2 minutes, then on medium until soft peaks form. Gently fold whipped cream into chestnut mixture. Cover and chill. Spoon chestnut mixture into shells and top with whipped cream and chocolate shavings.

Coconut Carrot Cake

2 cups all-purpose flour

2 teaspoons cinnamon

1½ teaspoons baking soda

1 teaspoon salt

2 cups sugar

1½ cups canola oil

4 eggs, room temperature

2 cups carrots, grated

1 cup flaked coconut

Preheat oven to 350°F. Grease and flour two 9-inch round cake pans. In a small bowl, stir together flour, cinnamon, baking soda, and salt. Set aside. In a large bowl, mix together sugar and oil until well blended. Beat in eggs, one at a time, mixing well after each addition. Stir in flour mixture until combined. Fold in carrots and coconut. Pour batter into prepared pans. Bake 30 minutes or until toothpick inserted in center comes out clean. Cool thoroughly in pans on cooling rack. Frost with your favorite cream cheese icing. See Week Six for icing recipe. <u>Note</u>: See Week Six for icing recipe.

KEEPING CHRIST IN CHRISTMAS

"For unto us a child is born, unto us a Son is given; and the government will be upon His shoulder. And His name will be called Wonderful, Counselor, Mighty God, Everlasting Father, Prince of Peace." Isaiah 9:6, NKJV[20]

Family Memories

Christmas time is when families gather to celebrate Christ's birth and exchange gifts. With every passing year, traditions are formed and memories are created for one and all. Below are creative ideas for establishing family traditions and creating special memories.

- At the end of November, let the children make a red-and-green chain with twenty-five loops representing the twenty-five days leading up to Christmas. Number each loop and place a verse related to Christmas on each. Every morning leading up to Christmas, have the children remove one loop and read the verse aloud as a family. You might want to reference the verses from the Christmas story from Matthew 1 and 2, dividing the story among the twenty-five loops.

- Make a JOY box for your family. Wrap a box in gold paper with a red-and-green bow. Put small sheets of paper and a pen beside the box under your tree. From December 1st until Christmas Day, family members can write answers to prayers, blessings, and things or names of people that have brought JOY to their lives this past year and place in box. On Christmas Day, open the box and share what was written. It will bless your family and bring JOY to your Christmas.

- The evening you put up your tree, talk about Christmas and why we celebrate. When placing the nativity, be sure to put it in a prominent place, not under the tree where it will be buried amidst packages. Put it in a place where it will be a constant reminder to your family of the reason we celebrate Christmas—Christ's birth!

- On Christmas Eve, make hot chocolate and serve a birthday cake for Jesus. Have Dad or Granddad read the Christmas story.

- On Christmas Eve Day, get the children involved in making costumes to act out the Christmas story that evening. Be creative and use items found around the house. Have the children act out the parts as Dad or Granddad reads the Christmas story.

- The wise men came bearing three gifts. To remove the focus from material things, and to keep from overspending, try this with your children this year. Give them each three gifts: one practical (clothing), one spiritual (Bible), and one fun (bike).

---

[20] Charles Stanley, *The Charles F. Stanley Life Principles Bible: New King James Version* (Thomas Nelson Publishing, 2005).

Christmas Creations

WREATHS

Begin with a grapevine wreath. Gather fresh greenery from your yard or a neighbor's yard; cedar is fragrant and is a wonderful look for this wreath. Starting at one point on the wreath, push cut boughs through the grapevine wreath. Continue placing boughs until complete. Use clippers to trim and shape. Add berries and pinecones, and hang on the front door. Materials needed: Grapevine wreath, eastern red cedar boughs, eastern red cedar berries, pinecones, smooth Sumac berries, wire as needed, and pruning shears. Note: Cut the boughs and soak them in water overnight. The next day, let them dry and then begin building your wreath. The extra hydration extends the life of the wreath. Any type of cedar and berry will work.

Begin with a grapevine wreath. Insert clusters of Nandina berries to cover wreath. Use strips of florist wire to hold them in place; the berries will hang a little loose due to the nature of the Nandina plant. Once berries are in place, use pruners to shape and, using wire, attach other items, such as kumquats, lemons, pears, rose hips, or Calamondin oranges—stems still attached. If fruit is without stems, use florist picks. Materials needed: Grapevine wreath, Nandina berries, Calamondin oranges, Meyer lemons, kumquats, rose hips, florist wire, florist picks, and hand pruners.

TOMATO CAGE TOPIARIES

Materials needed: Garden urn, number of wire tomato cages for height desired for each topiary, duct tape, green florist wire, evergreen garland (fresh or nice fake), cuttings of greenery (such as pine, fir, balsam, and cedar), mini tree lights, wide ribbon, dried pomegranates, pine cones, and artichokes. These cages retain their original finish, but you can spray paint them a color such as black, silver, gold, copper, or dark green.

- Step One: Invert the cages and join the tips of the wire using a thin strip of duct tape. Stack cages in a garden urn.

- Step Two: Cut a ten-foot piece of evergreen garland. Wire it to the top of the stack of tomato cages, and wrap it around the stacked cages several times. Use green florist wire to hold garland in place.

- Step Three: Wire different kinds of fresh greenery into garland for added fullness. Cover top edge of urn with additional greenery all the way to the bottom. Cut wide ribbon into fifteen-inch lengths, and insert it into greenery. Twist a twelve-inch piece of florist wire around the base of each pomegranate, pine cone, and artichoke, and then wire them at intervals to the greenery.

CHRISTMAS CANDLELIGHT

A single flame flickering in the night creates warmth and an intimate setting; a cluster of candles creates a collective array of sparkle. Ideas such as a tiered fireplace insert can create the warmest of settings for the holiday when lit candles are resting on each arm and the insert is set on a sideboard, at the front door, or within the fireplace itself. Fresh greenery and berries can be placed around the base of the fireplace insert for color and interest. Below are some ideas for creating warmth using candlelight this Christmas season:

- Do you want to find a use for those small sections of leftover gift wrap? Using small glass votive, take the leftover snippets of gift wrap paper and cover the outside of the votive. Cut the paper the width and length of the votive and secure paper edges with double-sticky tape. Tie coordinating ribbon around the votive. Fill with candles, candies, flowers, or greenery.

- A plant stand can double as a tall candelabrum. Fill small glass fishbowls or jars with cranberries and votive candles (or half can be filled with cranberries and red flowers to add more color). Place one bowl on each arm of the plant stand. Around outer base of the bowl, place sprigs of fresh greenery. Drape red ribbons down the inside pole of the plant stand. This creates a beautiful, warm welcome for guests when placed at the front entrance of your home.

- Line a porch railing, outdoor staircase, walkway, or mantle with clear mason jars or utility lamp covers. Tea lights placed inside make the glass sparkle and create a warm welcome. Fresh greenery and berries at the base add color and interest.

- Going with a Woodlands theme this Christmas, make these wood scrapbooking and wood wrapped candles. Materials needed: Pine bough, bark, print scrapbook paper, bark strips (found at craft stores e.g., Hobby Lobby, Michaels, etc.), natural twine, red twine, scissors, paper cutter, pillar candles (variety of sizes), glue dots, florist wire, wire cutters, and scissors. For bark print scrapbooking paper wrapped pillar candle: Cut the bark print scrapbooking paper to size of pillar candle. Using glue dots, secure the paper around the candle. Wrap the whole candle in the bark scrapbook paper. Cut a long length of natural twine and wrap it around the candle a couple times ending with a knot. Cut a piece of pine and secure with twine, tying a bow to hold it in place. For bark wrapped pillar candle: The bark comes in rolls and can be difficult to unroll. To help make the roll pliable, soak in water for two hours. Place each strip around a medium size Mason jar. Let dry before wrapping around candles (when wet it stains white candles). Cut the bark to the size needed, overlapping edges ¼ to ½ inch. Bark cuts easily with scissors. No adhesive is needed on the bark. Tie twine around it tightly and secure it in place. Using florist wire, add a pine piece with pine cone and tie a twine bow to cover wire. Place candles on candle holders or on stacks of wood slices to give height variations, then place in a wooden tray. Use as many pillars as you desire for table centerpiece or for coffee table décor. Place remaining pine, pine cones, and berries in bottom of tray. <u>Note</u>: Look for pine pieces with pine cones already attached. Alternate red and natural twine for a festive look. The bark and scrapbook paper are both easy to remove when you want to change the look of the candles.

- Crystal Mason jar lights are beautiful and an elegant edition to your Christmas décor. Materials needed: Mason Jars, Epsom salt, twine, picks (florist section of craft store), ModgePodge glue, acrylic spray, tea light candle, sponge brush, and a large bowl. Fill large bowl with the Epsom salt. Using sponge brush, paint the ModgePodge glue evenly over the entire surface of the jar. Holding the jar over bowl, sprinkle salt covering the wet glue and entire surface of jar. Allow to dry. Spray acrylic covering the Epsom salt and surface of jar. Allow to dry. Using twine, greenery, berries and small pine cones, decorate the jar. Place a small tea light inside and watch your crystal jar glow!

GIFT IDEAS

- Decorative cellophane bags neatly hold one or two paper white bulbs. Nestle the bulb in moist moss sheets, which will provide protection for the bulb and a saucer of moisture. Tie the bag with red decorative ribbon.

- Place a food item in a decorative jar and attach recipe to top along with a festive ribbon. Below are two recipes that are wonderful to give to neighbors, family, and friends.

Creamy Caramel Sauce

1 cup whipping cream

1½ cups light brown sugar, firmly packed

1 teaspoon vanilla

½ cup water

¼ cup butter

Bring whipping cream to a simmer in a large saucepan over medium heat, stirring occasionally. Remove from heat and cool. Bring brown sugar and water to a simmer over medium heat, stirring occasionally. Cover and increase heat to medium-high; cook two minutes. Uncover and cook, stirring occasionally, about five minutes or until mixture is golden brown. Remove from heat. Stir in cream mixture, butter, and vanilla. Cool. Store in an airtight container in refrigerator.

Cookies in a Jar

PLACE IN JAR:

1¾ cups all-purpose flour

¾ teaspoon baking soda

¾ teaspoon baking soda, and salt

1½ cups chocolate chips

¾ cup brown sugar, firmly packed

½ cup sugar

Combine flour, baking soda, and salt. Using 1 quart jar, place flour mixture in bottom. Layer remaining ingredients in order listed above, pressing firmly after each layer. Seal with lid and decorate with festive bow. Recipe to attach: Preheat oven to 350°F. Beat ¾ cup butter, 1 large egg, and ¾ teaspoon vanilla in large mixing bowl until well blended. Add cookie mix and ½ chopped pecans; mix well. Break up clumps. Once blended, drop by rounded tablespoons onto ungreased cookie sheet.

CHRISTMAS RECIPES

Eggnog Coffee Punch

1 quart coffee ice cream

1 quart vanilla ice cream

1 quart eggnog

2 cups hot brewed coffee, cooled

½ cup brewed coffee, very strong

Whipping cream, whipped stiff

2 tablespoons nutmeg

Scoop ice cream into punch bowl. Add eggnog; stir until ice cream is slightly melted. Mix in cooled coffees. Serve topped with whipped cream and a dash of nutmeg.

Crescent Pesto Appetizers

2 (8 ounce) cans Pillsbury crescent rolls

1 (6 ounce) jar pesto

½ cup Mozzarella cheese, grated

¼ cup butter, melted

¼ cup Parmesan cheese, grated

Preheat oven to 350°F. Separate each perforated portion of dough to make eight triangles. Cut each in half to make sixteen triangles. Mix pesto and Mozzarella cheese until well blended. Spoon 1½ teaspoons on each triangle and roll up; start at wide end. Place on lightly greased cookie sheet. Brush each roll with melted butter and sprinkle with Parmesan cheese. Bake for 15 to 20 minutes until golden brown. Remove rolls to wire rack and serve immediately.

Cheddar and Tomato Spread

1 (10 ounce) can Rotel tomatoes

1 cup mayonnaise

2 teaspoons Worcestershire sauce

2 (8 ounce) blocks sharp Cheddar cheese, shredded

1 (4 ounce) jar chopped pimento, drained

Stir together first three ingredients. Mix in cheese and pimento. Serve with crackers or raw vegetables.

Barbecue Meatballs

2 cups barbecue sauce

1 cup prepared mustard

1 cup honey

2 teaspoons onion powder

2 teaspoons garlic powder

2 teaspoons lemon rind, grated

4 tablespoons lemon juice, fresh

½ teaspoon Worcestershire sauce

1 (32 ounce) package frozen Italian-style meatballs, thawed

Cook barbecue sauce and next seven ingredients in a Dutch oven over medium heat for 5 minutes, stirring often. Add meatballs; bring to a boil. Reduce heat and simmer for 30 minutes. Serve hot.

Artichoke Cheesecake

¼ cup fine breadcrumbs

½ cup Parmesan cheese, grated

2 tablespoons dried Italian seasoning

2 (8 ounce) packages cream cheese, softened

1 (14 ounce) jar artichoke hearts, drained and chopped

1 cup Feta cheese, crumbled

3 large eggs

1 (8 ounce) sour cream

¾ cup sweet red pepper, diced

¾ cup green pepper, diced

1 large garlic clove, minced

1 teaspoon dried tarragon

2 teaspoons dried basil

Garnish: fresh tarragon

Preheat oven to 375°F. Generously butter a springform pan. Combine first three ingredients; coat bottom of pan with breadcrumb mixture., and set aside remaining mixture. Process cream cheese in a food processor until smooth, stopping to scrape down sides. Add chopped artichokes and next eight ingredients to processor bowl. Stir well. Pour mixture into pan. Bake uncovered for 45 to 50 minutes until golden brown. Cool completely in pan on a wire rack. Chill at least 2 hours. Carefully remove sides from springform pan. Pat reserved breadcrumb mixture on sides of cheesecake. Garnish, if desired. Serve with toast points or assorted crackers.

Chocolate Peppermint Parfaits

2 cups whipping cream, divided

2 large whole eggs

2 egg yolks

¼ cup sugar

6 (1 ounce) semisweet chocolate squares, melted

3 tablespoons brewed coffee, strong and cooled

½ teaspoon peppermint extract

⅓ cup crushed hard peppermint candies

½ cup cream-filled sandwich cookie crumbs

GARNISH: Crushed hard candy pieces. Whisk together 1 cup whipping cream, whole eggs, egg yolks, and sugar in small heavy saucepan until well blended. Cook, whisking constantly, over medium-low heat 10 to 12 minutes or until mixture reaches 160°F. Remove from heat and pour through a wire-mesh strainer into bowl and let cool. Whisk in melted chocolate, coffee, and peppermint extract. Beat remaining 1 cup whipping cream until soft peaks form; fold in crushed candy. Spoon 1 tablespoon of cookie crumbs into each of 6 (6 ounce) parfait glasses; top each with 2 tablespoons chocolate mixture and 2 tablespoons whipped cream. Repeat layers. Cover and chill 3 hours. Garnish and serve.

Nutty Cinnamon Palmiers

1 (17 ounce) package frozen puff pastry sheets, thawed

1 large egg

1 tablespoon water

1 tablespoon ground cinnamon

½ cup sugar

½ cup pecans, finely chopped

Preheat oven to 400°F. Unfold pastry sheets; roll each sheet into 16x12 triangles. Combine egg and water, brush pastry with half of the mixture. Combine cinnamon, sugar, and nuts, sprinkle over pastry. Start at short end and roll each pastry up tightly, jelly roll fashion, meeting in the center. Each pastry should resemble a scroll. Brush with remaining egg mixture. Cut each into half-inch slices and place 2 inches apart on greased cookie sheet. Bake for 10 minutes or until golden brown.

Pumpkin Tart

CRUST:

1¼ cup all-purpose flour

½ teaspoon salt

½ cup butter, cut in pieces

¼ teaspoon ground ginger

3-4 tablespoons cold water

½ teaspoon cinnamon

FILLING:

1 (15 ounce) can pumpkin

½ cup sugar

1 teaspoon ground ginger

2 teaspoons vanilla

2 teaspoons cinnamon

2 large eggs, slightly beaten

½ cup whipping cream

STREUSEL:

¾ cup all-purpose flour

⅓ cup brown sugar, firmly packed

1 teaspoon salt

¼ cup cold butter, cut into pieces

Preheat oven to 375°F. Stir together flour and salt in mixing bowl.; cut in butter with pastry blender or fork until coarse crumbs form. Mix ginger and cinnamon with fork, adding enough water until flour is just moistened. Pat into ungreased 10 inch tart pan with removable bottom or 9-inch glass pie pan. Bake for 10 to 15 minutes or until crust is lightly browned. Combine pumpkin, sugar, ginger, vanilla and cinnamon in a large bowl. Stir in slightly beaten eggs until blended. Stir in whipping cream. Pour pumpkin mixture into baked crust. Cover edges of crust with aluminum foil. Bake for 30 to 35 minutes or until set around the edges. Mix streusel: flour, brown sugar, salt and cinnamon in small bowl. Cut in butter until coarse crumbs form. Sprinkle streusel over top of hot, partially baked filling. Continue baking 15 to 20 minutes or until knife inserted comes out clean. Cool 30 minutes and top with fresh whipped cream.

Praline Coffee

3 cups hot brewed coffee

¾ cup half and half

¼ to ½ cup light brown sugar, firmly packed

¾ cup praline flavoring

Sweetened whipped cream

Heat first three ingredients in large saucepan over medium heat, stirring constantly, until thoroughly heated. Do not boil. Stir in praline flavoring and serve topped with sweetened whipped cream.

Mary's Christmas Morning Orange Julius

1 (6 ounce) can frozen orange juice concentrate

½ cup milk

1 cup water

¼ cup sugar

½ cup half and half

10 ice cubes

Thoroughly blend in a blender and serve in chilled glasses. Enjoy!

Christmas Punch

⅓ cup white sugar

2 cups unsweetened pineapple juice

1 quart cranberry juice

3 tablespoons almond extract

1 (2 liter) bottle Ginger Ale

In a large container, mix together sugar, pineapple juice, cranberry juice, and almond extract. Refrigerate for 1 day in order for flavors to blend. To serve, pour juice mixture into a punch bowl. Stir in Ginger Ale. Float cranberries on top.

Apple Cranberry Punch

1 (32 ounce) bottle apple juice, chilled

1 (12 ounce) can frozen cranberry juice concentrate

1 cup orange juice

1½ liters Ginger Ale

1 apple, sliced

In a large punch bowl, combine apple juice, cranberry juice concentrate, and orange juice. Stir until dissolved, then slowly pour in the Ginger Ale. Thinly slice the apple vertically, forming whole apple slices Float slices on top of punch.

What I Learned Today

Decorating and Gift Ideas
for Thanksgiving and Christmas ...

Creative Ideas for Applying Spiritual Application
to Our Family Holiday Celebrations ...

STUDENT BOOK REFERENCE LIST

A Collection of Favorite Recipes by Cherry House Furniture Galleries. Kearney, NE: Morris Press. 2001.

American Heart Association, "How to Read a Nutrition Label." www.heart.org/HEARTORG/Getting Healthy/NutritionCenter/Nutrition-Center UCM 001188 SubHomePage.jsp

Bellican, Dr. Bill. "The Family Meal for the Holidays ... Or Every Day? *Mid-South Families,* November 2010.

Goldman, Marcy. *A Passion for Baking.* Birmingham: Oxmoor House Publishing, 2007.

Higgs, Liz Curtis. *Bad Girls of the Bible and What We Learn from Them.* Colorado Springs: Waterbrook Press, 2000.

Katz, David. *The Way to Eat.* Naperville, IL: Sourcebooks, Inc., 2002.

Lewis, Robert. *The New Eve.* Nashville: B&H Publishing Group, 2008.

Marantha! Music. "Give Thanks," 1988. *Praise 10: O Lord, My Lord.*

May, Iva. *W3: Woman, Worldview and the Word.* Chronological Bible Discipleship, 2007. Revised 2010.

Peel, Kathy. "Is Your Kitchen User Friendly?" *HomeLife,* March 2011.

Secrets from the Southern Living Test Kitchens. Birmingham: Oxmoor House Inc., 2002.

Stanley, Charles. *The Charles F. Stanley Life Principles Bible: New King James Version.* Nashville: Thomas Nelson Publishing, 2005.

The Taste of Home Cookbook. Reiman Media Group Inc. 2009.

USDA, "Fact Sheets, Safe Food Handling, Freezing and Food Safety." www.fsis.usda.gov/FactSheets/ Focus On Freezing/index.asp

THE AUTHOR

Dianne Dougharty was married to her high school sweetheart for forty-five years. After an extended illness, Mark went to be with Jesus on July 31, 2018. She is the mother of two daughters and Mimi to seven grandchildren. Dianne graduated from Trevecca Nazarene University with a degree in Elementary Education. For over twenty years, she has led women's Bible studies, spoken at conferences, authored curriculum, and contributed written work to several blogs. She faithfully served for years beside her husband in full-time vocational ministry.

Dianne has a desire to see older women fulfill the mandate given them in Titus 2:3-4, "These older women must train the younger women to love their husbands and their children, to live wisely and be pure, to work in their homes, to do good, and to be submissive to their husbands. Then they will not bring shame to the word of God." NLT

Her heart is for young women to become seekers of Christ, students of God's Word, and lovers of their home, husband, family, and calling. She has a passion to see women live purposefully—making investments in the lives of other women.

God led Dianne to develop the Secrets Savored Ministry, a fun hands-on approach to developing community among women who desire to create a spirit of hospitality and Christlikeness within their lives, homes, and relationships—for the glory of God! Once a week, small groups meet within home settings and learn to apply biblical principles for living a godly life in an often God-less world.

Check out the ministry at secretssavored.org.
Follow her on Facebook, Twitter, and Pinterest.

SECRETS *Savored*

CREATING COMMUNITY

THROUGH SIMPLE HOSPITALITY

Secrets Savored is a Titus 2 discipling tool. Women across generations discover the treasure of community as they practice simple hospitality and apply Biblical truths in a home setting. This in-depth Bible study is growing women into a deeper faith and building Christ-like character within them.

Follow Us: @SECRETSSAVORED

Secrets Savored
PARTICIPATION INFO SHEET

NAME: _____

SINGLE: _____

MARRIED: 1–5 years _____ 6–10 years _____ More than 10 years _____

AGE: 15–22 _____ 23–30 _____ 31–35 _____ over 35 _____

E-MAIL: _____

ADDRESS: _____

_____

_____

CELL PHONE: _____

WORK PHONE: _____

ALLERGIES: _____

Tell us about yourself: Example: Where did you go to school? Where do you work? Where did you grow up? Do you have any unusual life experiences? Do you have any children? If so, how many and what are their ages?

Made in the USA
Columbia, SC
07 September 2022

66671039R00115